THE WIDE HORIZONS READERS

CURRICULUM FOUNDATION SERIES

WIDE HORIZONS

BOOK 3

Helen M. Robinson
Marion Monroe
A. Sterl Artley
Charlotte S. Huck
William A. Jenkins
Ira E. Aaron

Scott, Foresman and Company

Acknowledgments

The Limerick Trick
Copyright © 1964 by Scott Corbett.
From *The Limerick Trick* by Scott Corbett,
by permission of Little, Brown and Co.—
Atlantic Monthly Press and Willis Kingsley Wing.

Skippack School
Skippack School by Marguerite de Angeli.
Copyright 1939 by Marguerite de Angeli.
Reprinted by permission of the author
and Doubleday & Company, Inc., and
The World's Work (1913) Ltd., London.

Philippe's Hill
Philippe's Hill by Lee Kingman.
Copyright 1950 by Mary Lee Natti.
Reprinted by permission of Doubleday & Company, Inc.

A Penny's Worth of Character
A Penny's Worth of Character by Jesse Stuart,
illustrated by Robert Henneberger.
Copyright 1954 Jesse Stuart and Robert Henneberger.
Used by permission of the Publisher, McGraw-Hill
Book Company.

Child of the Silent Night
Child of the Silent Night, Copyright © 1963
by Edith Fisher Hunter, with illustrations
and jacket by Bea Holmes; used by permission
of the publisher, Houghton Mifflin Company.

Macaroon
Macaroon, by Julia Cunningham, illustr. by Evaline Ness.
© Copyright 1962 by Julia Cunningham and
Evaline Ness. Reprinted by permission of
Pantheon Books, a Division of Random House, Inc.,
and George Harrap & Co., Ltd., London.

Photograph
Marguerite de Angeli, page 80, photograph by Clara E. Sipprell.

2

Contents

On Opening a New Book

Here's an adventure! What awaits
Beyond these closed, mysterious gates?
Whom shall I meet, where shall I go
Beyond the lovely land I know?
Above the sky, across the sea?
What shall I learn and feel and be?
Open, strange doors, to good or ill!
I hold my breath a moment still
Before the magic of your look.
What will you do to me, O Book?

—Abbie Farwell Brown

Did you ever think what a book can do to you?
It can make you feel as you have never felt before.
It can make you happy or sad, fill you with wonder,
and teach you new things. Through the pages of
a book you can visit places you've never seen
before, meet people you'd never have a chance to
meet in any other way. A book can take you back
in time to when your great-great-grandparents lived,
or it can spin you through your imagination to a
world in which you can talk with animals and
animals can talk with you.

5

But you will say, "No one book can do all that!" And you will be right, of course; but also wrong. For *this book* does do all these things. However, *Wide Horizons*, Book Three, is unusual—it contains five complete books and one-half of another. Each of these selections is meant to be enjoyed along with or following one of the groups of stories in your Basic Reader. As you read, you will want to keep a *Wide Horizons* notebook for yourself. Put in it everything that you are asked to write, as well as any ideas that you would like to save and share with others. You may also want to write down in it the names of other books that you have read and have especially enjoyed.

The first selection in *Wide Horizons* is one that will make you laugh. It includes the first five chapters of Scott Corbett's book *The Limerick Trick*. If you want to find out if Kerby ever gets rid of his habit of talking in verse, you will have to get a copy of the book and finish it yourself. The author has written five other stories about Kerby, his dog Waldo, and his friend Fenton that you may want to read also.

In the book *Skippack School*, the author takes you back in time to a few years before the American

Revolution. Much in this story is true. There really was a kind schoolmaster by the name of Christopher Dock and a printer in Germantown called Master Sauer. The schoolmaster wrote a book describing the way he taught, and his friend printed it. When Marguerite de Angeli decided to write a story about these Mennonite settlers, she used Master Dock's book and included people in her story who lived at that time and in that place. Then she made up the story of Eli Shrawder and his family who could have had these many adventures. When an author tells a story based upon known facts that really happened in the past, but includes some imaginary characters and events, we call it historical fiction. Marguerite de Angeli was just as careful to have her pictures correctly portray the way these people lived as her story does.

If you like to ski, you will enjoy reading *Philippe's Hill* by Lee Kingman. In this book Philippe Tourneau is as ingenious and creative as Eli Shrawder, but his story takes place today in the Laurentian Mountains in Canada. Even though Miss Kingman made up the story, it could really happen. Therefore we call it realistic fiction.

A Penny's Worth of Character by Jesse Stuart takes place in the country in the days before washing machines and supermarkets. What Shan learns in this story is not old-fashioned, however. It might still be learned by anyone collecting the deposit on a cracked pop bottle. Notice how the illustrations in this book reflect Shan's change of mood.

A biography tells the story of a person's life. *Child of the Silent Night* by Edith Fisher Hunter is the story of Laura Bridgman, the first deaf and blind child to be taught to "talk" and "hear" with her hands. All of us have heard about Helen Keller, but most of us do not know about Laura Bridgman, who learned to read and write and "talk" some fifty years before Helen Keller did.

If someone in your family, or your teacher, has read you *Winnie the Pooh* or *Charlotte's Web*, then you already know how much fun animal fantasy can be. *Macaroon* by Julia Cunningham is the story of a smart raccoon who allows himself to be adopted every year by a child. That way he does not have to sleep in a tree all winter. He is pleased with this plan except that he hates to leave the children in the spring. One year he decides to find the most impossible child in the town and allow her to adopt him. Then he thinks he will enjoy leaving her. You will want to read this story to see if Macaroon's plans work out the way he thought they would.

You now know something more about the six stories within this book. You have some clues to help you answer the question

          . . . What awaits
Beyond these closed, mysterious gates?

But remember you were warned—a book can change you. When you finish reading these books, you may not be the same person you were. Certainly you should be a better reader, and you will have had many new and exciting adventures. And now

    Open, strange doors, to good or ill!

Scott Corbett, the author of *The Limerick Trick,* grew up in a Midwestern city much like the one he writes about in this book. Just like Kerby Maxwell, he played in a small, woodsy park and in a vacant lot with a clubhouse in it. His adventures, however, were not quite so interesting as Kerby's.

While he was in college, Scott Corbett began to write jokes and sell them to magazines for a couple of dollars apiece. After college he went to New York City to become a writer. He wrote stories for magazines, radio, and television for many years and then began to write books for children. He has now published fifteen of these, including five "Trick" books about Kerby and his friends.

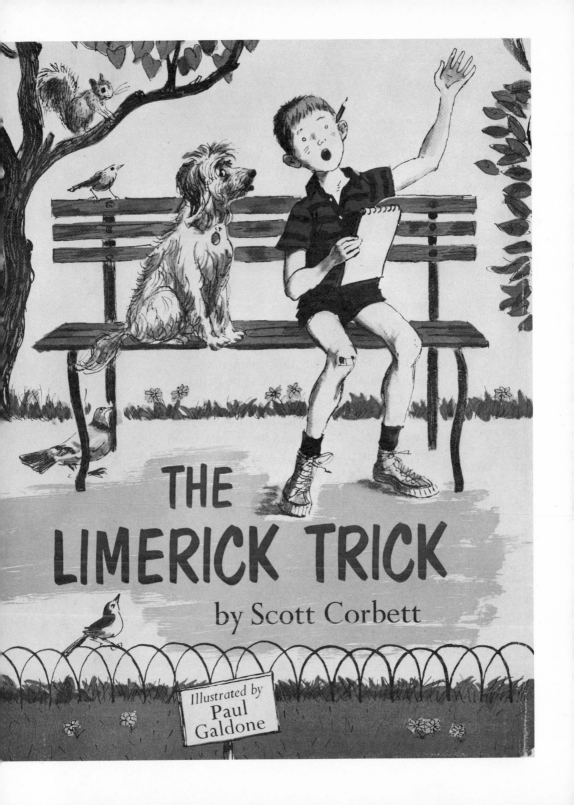

THE
LIMERICK TRICK

by Scott Corbett

Illustrated by
Paul
Galdone

In Kerby's school there was to be a
poetry contest with an English bicycle
as a prize. What happened to Kerby
in his effort to win this prize makes
an unusual and amusing story. It is
hard to believe that you will ever have
an experience like Kerby's, but maybe
one of your own experiences has been
as helpful to you as Kerby's was to him.

THE LIMERICK TRICK

by SCOTT CORBETT

Illustrated by PAUL GALDONE

An Atlantic Monthly Press Book
LITTLE, BROWN AND COMPANY
Boston • Toronto

To Elizabeth
with love

(I wanted it this way, it's true,
But also it happens I knew
That Waldo and Kerby
Would like to have her be
The one that this story is to.)

14

Chapter One

The center of the vacant lot was exactly the right place for the boys' clubhouse. It was the same distance from all three houses. The vacant lot was behind Kerby Maxwell's house, while Fenton Claypool lived on one side of it and Bumps Burton on the other.

They had built their clubhouse with old lumber some workmen had given them. It was not much to look at. It leaned. Its door was so small they had to crawl inside. And inside there was barely room enough for the three of them. In fact, just to show how little room there was, Kerby's dog Waldo had to stay outside. This always annoyed Waldo, because he considered himself a member of the club.

Bumps Burton was the club president. Before the church pageant last spring, Bumps had been a big bully that nobody liked. Everyone made fun of him behind his back for being so big and awkward, and Bumps paid them back by being mean. For example, he would not let anybody else play in the vacant lot. If Kerby so much as walked through it on his way home, Bumps would twist his nose— and when Bumps twisted a nose, he did a thorough job of it. But after trouble at their pageant rehearsal, when the three boys had fought side by side against some of the other choirboys, the three had made friends and built their clubhouse.

Today, the minute they got home from school, Bumps called a meeting.

"Something important," he growled, looking angry.

It was a sharp, chilly September afternoon, with sullen clouds scudding across the sky. They were glad to crawl inside out of the wind.

"No, Waldo," said Kerby. Waldo had to sit just outside the door, frowning in at them.

The three boys sat down on their boxes, and Bumps wasted no time coming to the point.

"I called a meeting because I think there's gonna be trouble tomorrow night at choir rehearsal."

16

Kerby and Fenton exchanged a not altogether surprised glance. Of course, Fenton was hard to surprise, anyway. Fenton was always thinking, usually one step ahead of everybody else.

"I'll bet it's that new boy," he said.

"Right," said Bumps. "Red Blake. He's been talking big about how we got no right to have a clubhouse here and not let anybody else be a member."

"Well, I'd like to know why not!" cried Kerby. "Don't we *live* here? I mean, nobody else lives right beside this lot, like we do!"

"Course not," agreed Bumps. "But all the same, Red Blake has been getting pretty chesty about it. He thinks he's tough. I guess it's his red hair."

"He *is* pretty big, too," Kerby noted. "Almost as big as you, Bumps."

"Well, we'll show *him* if he gets wise. But we got to stick together tomorrow night and be ready for anything."

Fenton Claypool's face had been its usual long, solemn self as he listened to them. Now one of his quick grins flashed across it.

"Poor old Miss Pease would really have another fit if we had a free-for-all again at one of her rehearsals! She's just barely forgiven us for the last one."

Miss Pease was their long-suffering church organist and choir director. At the thought of her they all burst out laughing.

"Oh, it won't come to a fight, I'm sure," Fenton added, "but I think Bumps is right—there may be a lot of tough talk. Of course, we might want to have somebody else in our club sometime, but we certainly don't need any Red Blake to tell us when."

This brought a warlike yell of agreement from Bumps and Kerby that made the clubhouse vibrate like a reed, and with that the meeting broke up.

"This place is still too shaky," Bumps grumbled as he led the procession outside—being president, he was always allowed to crawl out first. "I think it needs a few more nails in it."

As they stood outside discussing problems of construction, a small old man came walking briskly down the street carrying a cane in one hand and a little black notebook in the other. He seemed to use the cane for swinging more than anything else, and he was muttering to himself as he studied the notebook.

He stopped, looked this way and that at Fenton's and Bumps' houses, and snapped his notebook shut as though satisfied. Then he glanced in the direction of the boys and their clubhouse under the lone tree in the center of the lot, and his head jerked back so hard his small brown felt hat almost fell off.

"Here, now!" he cried in a high, annoyed voice, and bustled straight toward them, tapping his cane hard on the ground at every step. He planted himself in front of the wide-eyed boys and prodded the clubhouse with his cane so sharply that it shivered in every timber.

"Who gave you permission to erect this eyesore on my property?"

"Y-your property, sir?" stammered Kerby. He had never before thought of the lot as being anybody's property.

"Yes, my property! Property of Alfred J. Carmody, that's what it is, and I'm Carmody. I've been out of town for a few years, but now I'm back to look things over, and right away I see something I don't like. This slapped-together scrap heap—I won't have it!" he declared, giving the clubhouse another dangerous prod. "Makes the property look

ridiculous. You'll have to remove it, every splinter and nail of it, and I want it done by Saturday, do you hear? And I'll be back to see that it's done, too!"

"But, sir——"

"Not a word, not a word!" cried the old man, waggling the rubber tip of his cane under their noses with a ferocity that made them jump back. "I haven't the time to argue, nor the inclination, either. Take it down—and do it by Saturday," he ordered over his shoulder as he turned and stamped off. "By Saturday!" he repeated, and thumped away down the street, leaving the boys speechless, stunned by sudden disaster.

Chapter Two

When they had recovered their breath and their senses, Kerby looked around at the others.

"What do we do now?"

"I don't know," said Fenton in a bleak voice. "I guess we tear it down."

"Aw, the heck with him," blustered Bumps. "He's probably just bluffing. I'll bet he doesn't even own this lot. He's just some crazy old man who doesn't like kids to have clubhouses."

"Maybe," said Fenton, "and maybe not."

Each of them, without thinking about it, was touching the clubhouse, feeling the grain of its weathered boards, or picking lovingly at one of its countless splinters, and each of them was gazing at it with stricken eyes. Tear down their club-house? Maybe it did not look like much, maybe it was no Mount Vernon or Taj Mahal, but it meant a lot to them. The times they had rushed into it during a rainstorm and it had kept them practically dry! The summer nights they had roasted weenies and marshmallows over the camp-fire in the little circle of stones outside it. The time Kerby and Fenton were going to sleep out in it all night, and Waldo got lost. So much had happened in and around their clubhouse. It was theirs, and they would be lost without it.

Fenton's mother came out of their house and called him.

"Coming, Mom! . . . Well, I've got to leave, fellows. I have to go downtown. We'll talk about it some more later."

Then Kerby heard a familiar motor. Above the board fence that separated his back yard from the vacant lot, he could see the top of his family's car come around the corner of the house and stop in front of the garage.

"There's my folks. See you later, Bumps," he said, and ran to the fence to push the loose board aside and slip through.

His father had left his office early because they had to go to a wedding. Kerby hurried to him, eager to ask a question. "Hi, Pop! Hi, Mom!"

"Hello, Son," said Mr. Maxwell, putting an arm around him as they walked toward the house. "Come on up and talk to me while I change clothes. What's new?"

"Plenty! Listen, Pop, have you ever heard of anybody called Alfred J. Carmody?"

Mr. Maxwell laughed briefly.

"Old A. J.? I'll say I have. But why? What about him?"

The way his father had laughed bothered Kerby. He followed him upstairs and into the bedroom with a sinking heart.

"He owns our vacant lot."

"He does? How do you know?"

"He just came by and told us so."

"What?" cried Mr. Maxwell, and nearly fell over taking off his trousers. "Alfred J. Carmody came by, in person?"

"Yes."

"When?"

"Just a few minutes ago. And he called our clubhouse an eyesore and told us to take it down. By Saturday."

Mr. Maxwell sat down on the side of the bed, staring at Kerby with incredulous eyes in which

belief slowly gathered. Kerby's mother stood in the doorway, listening. Waldo looked around at all of them and then flopped down on the floor, unable to make head or tail of any of it.

"Well, that sounds just like him, all right," said Kerby's father.

He stood up, pulled off his shirt and put on a clean one, and stood looking out the bedroom window while he buttoned it up. Then he shook his head and sighed.

"Well, of course, Kerby," he said, "we have to admit that your clubhouse is hardly a beautiful piece of architecture. It does look more like a packing case that's been through a train wreck. Still, if he were anybody else, I'd be tempted to get together with the Claypools and Burtons and send him a petition. But not Alfred J. Carmody. From what I've heard of him, it wouldn't do a bit of good."

Mr. Maxwell moved away from the window.

"He's a very wealthy man," he continued. "He owns a lot of real estate here in town. Matter of fact, I read in the paper only yesterday that he's here on a visit to look over his property. First time he's been here in several years."

Kerby's mother glanced at her watch. "I'm sorry, dear, but if you don't get a move on, we'll be late."

"All right, I'll hurry. We'll discuss old A. J. later."

"We'll be home by suppertime, Kerby."

"Okay, Mom. Okay if I go to the park for a while?"

"Yes, but don't be late. Have you worked on your poem for school?"

Kerby groaned. "That's what I'm going to do. That stupid old poem!"

"Keep after it, and you'll think of one."

Kerby sighed loudly and went to his room for a pocket notebook and pencil. After a moment's hesitation, he also stuffed Waldo's leash into another pocket of his shorts. He and Waldo grabbed a ride with his parents to the park, but then instead of sitting down somewhere and trying to think of his poem, Kerby put the leash on Waldo and crossed over to Park Square. He wanted one more look at the reason he was so eager to write the best poem of all.

The reason was to be found in the window of the Park Square sporting goods store. It was a magnificent English bicycle with a sign in front of it that said:

FIRST PRIZE

This Bicycle, or a Gift Certificate valued at $42.50, will be awarded to the winner of the Third Annual City-Wide Elementary Schools Poetry Contest. The Award will be made by Mayor Chester B. Dorgan at Slagle Junior High School Auditorium, Oct. 1, at 3:00 P.M. *Donated by* FRIENDS OF POETRY SOCIETY, *Mrs. Marshall T. Cowbell, President.*

Kerby had not said a word to anybody about it, but he wanted that bicycle more fiercely than anything he had ever wanted in his whole life. The reason he had said nothing about it was that he could not imagine anything more unlikely than for him to write any poem at all, let alone a good one. Let alone a better one than thousands of other children all over the city!

Every child in the top three grades had to write a poem. Then each class was to choose its own best poem and submit it to the contest. Here it was Thursday, and their poems had to be turned in to Miss McFee on Monday, and so far he had not been able to write even a punk poem. Nevertheless, standing in front of the big display window, he lost himself in a dream of winning the beautiful bicycle. Sitting beside him none too patiently, looking in the window, too, Waldo yawned.

"Isn't that a beauty, Waldo?" murmured Kerby. "Can't you just imagine what it would be like to ride it?"

Personally, Waldo did not care particularly for bicycles, and certainly he would not have cared to ride on one. Furthermore, he was eager to get back to the park, where he could run free and chase squirrels. Whenever they took a walk where there was a lot of traffic, he had to have his leash on, but like any normal, self-respecting dog Waldo hated leashes. He stood up and gave a little tug on it now. Just a suggestion.

"Okay, okay," sighed Kerby. "Let's go."

They returned to Peterson Park, the small but woodsy public park where Kerby and his friends often played. Set free, the small, flop-eared dog, still part puppy, went racing away happily among the trees to look for squirrels. Kerby followed moodily, head down, thinking about all his troubles and wondering why things never worked out the way you wanted them to. Why couldn't he write a poem? Fenton had already written two. Even Bumps had written one, though it was terrible. And of course Irma Mosley had probably written hers days ago. Everybody expected Irma to write the best one in their class, because she always did. But why couldn't he write a poem, too?

Well, for one thing, it was too much trouble. It was hard work, trying to write a poem!

Reaching the path near the drinking fountain, Kerby stopped and had a drink. The only sounds around him were the rustle of trees and Waldo's barking in the distance. The benches were empty. Nobody wanted to sit around in the park when a chilly wind was making the first fall of autumn leaves leap into the air and do cartwheels along the path like crazy acrobats. Kerby had the park to himself.

The drinking fountain always made him think of his strange friend Mrs. Graymalkin, because it was there he had first met her. Mrs. Graymalkin was an odd old lady who wore odd clothes—a big hat with an enormous feather trailing from it, a draggly black cape over a draggly black dress, and high-heeled shoes. Her laugh sounded like a whole barnyard full of chickens, and her teeth fascinated him—there were so few of them, and so much space between them.

That first time he met her she had one of her high heels stuck in the grating of the drain beside the drinking fountain. He had helped her work it free. The next day she rewarded him with an old chemistry set she said had belonged to her son Felix when he was a little boy. And that chemistry set had certainly been full of surprises!

She had told him how to do that crazy lemonade trick that turned out so differently from what he expected, and then later on, when Waldo disappeared, she had told Kerby a way to use the chemistry set to help him find Waldo.

Since then he had not seen her. As he left the drinking fountain and walked on, Kerby wished he could see her again. Maybe she could tell him a way to write poetry! . . . But then he shook his head.

"Fat chance of *me* winning that old contest!" he growled aloud.

"What contest, Kerby?" asked a creaky voice.

Kerby nearly jumped out of his skin. He whirled around to find Mrs. Graymalkin standing directly behind him, peering down at him with twinkling eyes as she laughed her hen-cackle laugh.

"Oh, did I startle you, Kerby dear? I didn't mean to," she said, as if she were sorry. But Kerby knew very well she was pleased with herself. No question about it, she loved to act mysterious. But at the same time, how on earth had she managed to show up behind him without his hearing her? She was pretty amazing, at that.

"Gee, Mrs. Graymalkin, you sure surprised me! I was just thinking about you."

"Were you? Now, isn't that nice of you. I often think about you, too, Kerby. How is that dear little dog of yours, little Waldo? And your splendid friend Fenton?"

"They're both fine, thanks. Waldo is here somewhere."

"I thought I saw him racing round and round a tree a moment ago. Well, now, Kerby, I'm curious —why were you thinking about me just now?"

Kerby looked down and pushed a pebble around with his sneaker. He felt a strong urge to ask the very favor that had been in his mind, but it made him feel shy to think about doing it, especially when it was such a crazy one.

33

"Oh, I was just thinking."

"What were you thinking, Kerby?" Mrs. Graymalkin asked patiently.

"Well, I was thinking that maybe you could help me again."

"How?"

"I'm not sure you can, but the thing is, I'd like to win an English bicycle."

Mrs. Graymalkin cackled again, but in a strange way.

"Well, well, well! . . . I suppose we'd all like to win an English bicycle, when it comes to that," she said, which surprised Kerby, since he could not imagine Mrs. Graymalkin racing around on an English bicycle, or on any other kind of bicycle, for that matter. Her eyes narrowed. "And how do you plan to win this English bicycle?"

Kerby explained about the contest.

"Oh, I see. And have you tried to write your poem, Kerby?"

"Sure! I've tried and tried!"

"How long have you been trying?"

"Oh, for a long time."

"How long?"

"A week."

"Every day?"

"Well, no."

"Have you worked on it for hours at a time?"

"Well . . . no."

"How long?"

"Well . . . not very long, I guess. But I can't write a poem! I get bored!"

"I see," said Mrs. Graymalkin. "You don't want to work hard over it, and struggle with each word. You want an easy way. In fact, you don't even really care about writing a poem, but you *do* want to win the contest so that you can have the English bicycle. Is that it?"

"Well, yes, I suppose so," admitted Kerby, feeling a bit ashamed when she put it that way.

Mrs. Graymalkin laid her thinking finger alongside her nose. Kerby had decided that one of her long, bony fingers was her thinking finger, because she always seemed to put it beside her nose when she wanted to do some important thinking.

Her sharp glance glittered down at him.

"You still have your chemistry set safely hidden away?" she asked, and chuckled as Kerby turned red. Once he had accidentally admitted that he kept her gift hidden from his parents. He was afraid they might be worried if they knew he had an old chemistry set a stranger had given him.

"Yes, I've still got it."

"Good. Now, I'll tell you a trick that might help you." Carefully Mrs. Graymalkin described the two tubes of liquid he was to use, one of them so many slots from the left side of the box, and the other so many slots from the right. Three drops from the first tube and two drops from the second.

"Put them in one of the tiny glass bowls, mix them together with your finger, and rub them on your forehead," she said, rubbing one of her crooked fingers over the mesh of wrinkles that covered her own forehead. "Rub them in good, and maybe they'll help. Now I must get on with my walk, because it's the only exercise I get any more, and I must go home before long."

"Well, thanks, Mrs. Graymalkin! I'll try your trick right away!" cried Kerby. Waving to her, he raced away through the trees calling Waldo, who soon came running.

Together they sped toward home, but Kerby did not feel as though he were running at all. In his imagination the spinning wheels of the English bicycle were already underneath him.

Chapter Three

Kerby kept the chemistry set in his toy chest in the basement. Nobody ever opened the chest but Kerby, and even if someone had, the set was well hidden under all his old games and toys and building blocks.

Digging down in the chest, Kerby lifted out the long box and carried it over to his father's workbench. It was a dusty old box with no printing on the outside at all. But when he opened it, some faded printing in black and red letters came into view on the inside of the lid:

FEATS O' MAGIC CHEMISTRY SET
Instructive! Entertaining!
Hours of Amusement!
Astonish Your Friends!
Make Extra Money Giving Demonstrations!

In the box, each in its own slot, were a couple of dozen glass tubes with various amounts of liquid in them. Each tube had a faded label on it, and most of the liquids were so colorless that to look at them nobody could have told one from another.

In a separate section of the box there were several kinds of retorts, beakers, eyedroppers, and other utensils, including a couple of tiny glass bowls Kerby had not noticed before. He took out one of these and set it on the workbench.

As usual, when he secretly worked with his chemistry set, he felt a bit guilty. What would his parents think if they knew? But then, he was not doing anything wrong—he only wanted to write the best poem and make them proud of him . . . and win a special bicycle.

Carefully he counted off the correct number of slots from the left side, as Mrs. Graymalkin had told him to. Taking out the tube, he uncorked it and thrust in the tip of an eyedropper. He held the eyedropper over the tiny bowl and squeezed out three drops.

"One . . . two . . . three!"

Next he counted slots from the right side of the box, and located the other tube. Taking a fresh eyedropper, he drew a tiny amount of liquid from that one. Two drops plinked into the bowl.

"One . . . two!"

At least these chemicals did not fizz or boil or bubble or smoke—the way the chemical had last time, when he and Fenton were looking for Waldo. Kerby went to the sink and washed out the two eyedroppers and returned them to the box. Then he stood looking down at the bowl for a moment, feeling nervous.

Little prickles were running up and down his spine like cat's feet. Such strange things happened when he fooled around with the old chemistry set!

But then he thought about that beautiful English bicycle again, and took a deep breath. He reached in his pocket and pulled out the small notebook and pencil. Opening the notebook to a fresh page, he put it on the workbench and laid the pencil beside it. Kerby was all ready to write a poem.

"Okay, let's get going!" he said in a voice that sounded so loud and hollow it startled him. He dabbled his finger in the tiny bowl, mixing the chemicals together well. Lifting his hand to his forehead quickly, before he could lose his nerve, he moved his wet finger back and forth across it, rubbing the chemicals in hard.

For a few seconds his forehead felt hot and prickly. Alarmed, Kerby rushed over to grab an old mirror that stood on the shelf above the sink. He inspected himself with anxious eyes. What if he got a terrible rash? What if his forehead got a big red mark on it, and . . .

But it looked the same as ever.

What was more, Kerby felt the same as ever.

Returning to the workbench, he picked up the pencil and notebook and tried to think of a poem. He frowned at the ceiling, he frowned at the floor, he scratched his head, he scowled. He threw down his writing tools.

"Shucks! I can't think of a thing!"

He stared at Waldo for a moment. Waldo scratched himself slowly and reflectively, and stared back.

"Well, I must have done something wrong. Anyway, I'm going straight over to the park and check with Mrs. Graymalkin. I hope she's still there!"

Back went the chemistry set to its hiding place, and back into Kerby's pocket went the pencil and notebook. And less than five minutes later Kerby and Waldo were running among the trees again, looking for Mrs. Graymalkin.

She was nowhere to be seen. Kerby and Waldo walked the park from end to end without meeting anybody. Kerby walked past the drinking fountain, calling her name and then turning around quickly, hoping to find her behind him. But she was not there. Disappointed and discouraged, feeling as gloomy as the weather, Kerby shoved his hands into his pockets and plunked himself down on a park bench.

"There goes my bicycle," he said to Waldo—in his mind it had already become *his* bicycle.

He pulled out the pencil and notebook and glared at them. He was tempted to throw them in the trash can out of pure spite. They certainly were not much good to anybody unless he knew what to write.

Bzzz!

Kerby sat up straight. Strange thoughts were stirring in his head—strange, wonderful thoughts. Flipping open the notebook, he licked his pencil and began to write. Sitting there in the deserted park, with dark tree branches lashing back and forth above his head and with red and gold leaves swirling about his feet, Kerby could hardly write fast enough.

When he had finished, he turned through the three pages he had filled in the small notebook, and found it hard to believe his eyes. He had written a poem! And it was good, too, ten times as good as the best Irma Mosley had ever written. And it had not been any trouble at all. All he really had to do was sit there and hold the pencil.

"It worked!" Proudly he held out the notebook to Waldo. "Look at that. A real poem!"

Waldo sniffed the notebook politely, but seemed unimpressed. He turned and trotted off as if to say that sniffing around for squirrels was more entertaining.

"Wait'll Fenton hears about *this* one!" cried Kerby, putting his precious notebook back in his pocket with great care. His impulse was to go take another look, a gloating look this time, at his bicycle, but he decided not to. The first thing he wanted to do was take his poem straight home and put it away in a safe place. And maybe Fenton would be home by now. He could hardly wait to tell him what had happened.

"Come on, Waldo, let's go!"

He decided to go home along the street Bumps and Fenton lived on instead of his own, in case Fenton was home. As he and Waldo crossed over, an old man with a cane stood hesitating on the corner, looking around and grumbling to himself. With a shock Kerby realized he was face to face again with A. J. Carmody.

"Drat it, I've gotten all turned around here," he was muttering. "Where is that fool place, anyway?"

Noticing Kerby, he beckoned to him with a swipe of his cane.

"Here, boy! . . . Well!" His eyebrows shot up and his forehead wrinkled enough to make his small hat wiggle on his head as he recognized Kerby. "You're one of the eyesore boys, aren't ye?"

"I—I——"

"Well, never mind that now. I need some information."

"Yes, sir?"

"Can you tell me the way to Park Square?"
Bzzz!

As Mr. Carmody spoke these words, Kerby felt as if his forehead were covered with cold goose pimples. A strange sharp buzzing filled his head.

"Er—what, sir?"

With a snort of impatience the old man repeated his question.

"Can you tell me the way to Park Square?"

"Why, yes, sir; it's right over there. . . . Stop fidgeting so! It's not far to go—so you don't have to stand here and swear!" said Kerby.

They blinked at each other. It would have been hard to tell which was the more surprised. But in Alfred J. Carmody's case, surprise quickly gave way to rage. He leaned forward and glared into Kerby's face with his chin stuck out.

"Why, that rhymes! You're quite the young smart aleck, aren't ye, going around and answering folks in poetry. But you'd best mind your manners and not be so all-fired fresh when you do, or I'll make you dance. And while I'm at it, I'll warn you again—take that shanty of yours off my property and *stay off* my property from now on, or I'll have the police after you! Now get along, before I use this on you where it'll do the most good!" he finished, swishing his cane back and forth.

Kerby was so flabbergasted at himself that he could hardly move at first, but now he decided he had better take the hint the cane was giving him. He sprinted away with his head in a whirl and

Waldo at his heels with his tail between his legs, leaving the old curmudgeon to glower after them and mutter things about the younger generation.

Kerby had his faults, but being fresh to his elders was not normally one of them. He could not understand what had made him burst forth with that smart-aleck reply to Mr. Carmody. A feeling of deep uneasiness passed through him at the thought. He ran his hand across his forehead. Had he overdone the rubbing? What was wrong?

"Well, maybe it'll pass off," he thought as he ran. "Probably it won't last."

When Kerby reached the vacant lot, he could see that the car was not back in Fenton's driveway yet. In the middle of the lot the clubhouse was jiggling, indicating that someone was inside, probably someone big and awkward. Bumps! If Bumps knew what he had just done, how he had cooked their goose with old Mr. Carmody . . . ! Kerby all but tiptoed past the clubhouse, hoping that Bumps would not hear him. But then Waldo went and sneezed, and Bumps crouched down and stuck his head out.

"Hi, Kerby. Where you been?"

"Over to the park. What you doing?"

"Making some repairs. The heck with old man Carmody, I'm still going to fix things up." Bumps tapped his head, looking pleased with himself. "I've been using my bean."

Kerby was pleasantly surprised by this news, since brainwork was not usually Bumps' strong point.

"Good, Bumps. How?"

"I figured out where we need more nails, so as to make things really steady. By the way, I left my hammer around the corner. Grab it and hand me it, huh?"

Bzzz! The warning sounded again in Kerby's head.

"Er—what?"

"Hand me my hammer, I said."

"Try using your bean, instead! It's big and it's thick, and it's hard as a brick—so bang in the nails with your head!" retorted Kerby.

Bumps banged his head, all right. He was so astonished that he cracked it on the top of the low door as he sprang up to come outside.

"Ow!" He stood rubbing his head, and his brow drew together into a massive presidential frown that made Kerby tremble. Bumps was sizing up Kerby's nose with an ominous gleam in his eye, and his powerful nose-tweaking fingers were twitching.

"Kerby Maxwell, it's been a long time since I gave your beak a couple of turns," he remarked. "Maybe too long."

Kerby gulped. "Honest, Bumps, I don't know what got into me. It's—it's—I don't know what!"

"Well, you better watch it, if you don't want a sore beezer!"

"Okay, Bumps, I will."

"One more crack like that and you won't even be a member of the club."

"Okay, Bumps."

Scuttling away, Kerby slipped through the loose board in the fence and entered his own back yard. He was glad his parents were still gone. Upstairs in his own room he put the notebook away, safe and sound, in his desk drawer. At least he had *that* much to show for the fix he was in. He had a terrific poem that would win *any* contest. But otherwise, he had plenty to worry about. What kind of mess was he in this time? Why was it he had this strange urge to make a poem out of certain things people said to him?

And why did those poems have to be so smart-aleck that they nearly got him a cane-whack and a nose-tweak?

He fidgeted around in his room for a minute or two, frightened and upset. Then he thought of Fenton. If only he would come home! Kerby went to the window and looked out.

The Claypools' car was in the driveway. Rushing to the phone, Kerby called their house.

Fenton answered. "Hi, Kerby. I just got home this minute."

"I know. Listen, Fenton, I need to talk to you. Sneak over without letting Bumps see you. He's in the clubhouse."

"What's the matter? Did you have some trouble with Bumps?"

"Well, yes, but it's something worse than that. Much worse!"

"I'll be right over," said Fenton.

Chapter Four

Fenton Claypool was the smartest boy in Kerby's class, and also the politest; but in spite of these qualities, all the other children liked him. He was polite without being too nice, and he was smart without ever making anybody else feel stupid. He was thoughtful about the way he used his brains.

It would have taken a genius, however, to make any sense of the words that came bursting out of Kerby when Fenton arrived.

"Gee, Fenton, I've fixed things good now! Old Mr. Carmody will *really* be after us! But how was I to know, when Mrs. Graymalkin told me to rub the stuff on my forehead, that——"

"Wait a minute!" cried Fenton, and picked out the words that interested him most. "Mrs. Graymalkin? Did you meet her again?"

"Yes! And then——"

"Start with that. Tell me exactly what happened."

At last Kerby started where he should have—at the beginning. He told Fenton exactly how he had happened to meet her, even though it meant confessing his secret desire to write a poem good enough to win the bicycle.

"So she told you to mix two of the chemicals together and rub them on your forehead."

"Yes. Three drops of one and two drops of the other. At first I thought it wasn't going to work, but then when I went back to the park to look for her again, all at once it started working, and I wrote my poem."

"Can I see it?"

"Sure, but first let me tell you the rest of what happened. The bad part. The part about old Mr. Carmody."

When Fenton heard that part he looked like somebody who did not know whether to laugh or cry.

"Gee whillikers! That must have been something. I sure would have liked to see what he looked like when you said *that!*" declared Fenton, looking horrified and worried and yet snickering wildly at the same time. "I'm surprised he didn't fracture your skull with that cane of his."

"He would have, if I hadn't left in a hurry! Honest, Fenton, I don't know what got into me. But that's not all. Then I came on home, and saw Bumps."

He described what had happened when he saw Bumps. With that, Fenton's long face really began to crinkle around the corners of his straight, firm mouth. He sat forward with an eager twinkle in his eye.

"Can you remember exactly what you said to Bumps?"

"How can I forget?" groaned Kerby. "Bumps needed his hammer. He said, 'Grab it and hand me it, huh?' Right then I felt this buzzing in my head."

" 'Grab it and hand me it, huh?' " Fenton repeated thoughtfully. "Go on."

"I said, 'What?' And he said, 'Hand me my hammer, I said.' Then I said: 'Try using your bean, instead! It's big and it's thick, and it's hard as a brick—so bang in the nails with your head!' "

For an instant there was dead silence in the room. Then Fenton fell back on the window seat where he was sitting, and roared. He laughed until he had to wipe his eyes with his sleeve, and that was something for Fenton.

"Well, of course, you were right. His head *is* hard enough, but it wasn't very nice to say so right out loud," said Fenton, still grinning. "And not very safe, either."

"He came close to twisting my nose good, let me tell you!"

Fenton jumped up and prowled around the room, thinking.

"Let's hear that other one again," he said, stopping suddenly. "What you said to Mr. Carmody. Can you remember it exactly?"

"Well, almost, I think," said Kerby, and tried. After a couple of hesitations, he was able to remember it pretty accurately.

"Just what I thought. Amazing!" said Fenton, his eyes wide. "Kerby, do you realize what it is you've been making up?"

"No. What?"

"Limericks!"

"Limericks? What are they?"

"They're a special kind of poem. They have five lines—two long ones, two short ones, and a long one, and they're usually funny. Remember those nonsense verses by Edward Lear that Miss McFee read us? Some of those were limericks. I can even remember one I especially liked."

"Let's hear it."

Standing in the center of the room, Fenton began stroking an imaginary beard as he recited in a deep, silly voice:

There was an Old Man with a beard
Who said: "It is just as I feared!
Two Owls and a Hen,
Four Larks and a Wren
Have all built their nests in my beard."

Kerby grinned feebly.

"That's a good one," he admitted. Then the similarity of the rhythm really struck him. "My gosh! You mean to say that I've been talking *limericks?*"

"Yes. Both times, people happened to say something that made a good first line, with exactly the right rhythm and the right number of words. First

Mr. Carmody did, and then Bumps did. *'Can you tell me the way to Park Square?'* . . . *'Hand me my hammer, I said!'* . . . *'There was an Old Man with a beard . . .'* Even what Bumps said first —'Grab it and hand me it, huh?' See? They're all the same. And when somebody says something like that, it sets you off."

Fenton's scientific look crept onto his face then, and he glanced keenly at Kerby as he said, "That's really a fabulous trick."

"And I'd like to get rid of it quick. It's making me speak like some kind of freak. I'm so mad I could kick a thick brick!" cried Kerby.

"Kick a thick brick! A triple rhyme!" Fenton said admiringly. "That's pretty good."

"Aw, Fenton, you did that on purpose!"

"Well, yes, I did. I had to see for myself if it really worked."

"Well, now you know!"

"*Hmmm,* yes. Of course, it's always important to be absolutely certain, though," said Fenton, continuing to look far too much like a scientist experimenting in a laboratory to suit Kerby.

Fenton cleared his throat and added, "Let's try it once more, just to check."

"You're really a pain in the neck! If this doesn't stop, I may blow my top and become a *complete* nervous wreck!" cried Kerby. "Cut it out, will you?"

"Gee, this is fun! I could keep this up all day."

"Well, I couldn't, so stop it."

"All right, I'm convinced. All you need is a first line that will rhyme with something, and away you go," said Fenton, pulling at one of his prominent, cup-handle-shaped ears, as he sometimes did when he was thinking about something that excited him. "Listen, I want to try just one more thing."

"No! I'm worried enough as it is."

"But this is important."

"What's so important?"

Fenton was concentrating hard.

"Let me see. . . . *Hmm*. . . . Here, I've got it."

"Got what?"

"There once was an African elephant . . ." said Fenton.

Kerby held his breath, waiting. But he found he felt no impulse to say anything. No buzzing in his head set the wheels in motion. He let out his breath in relief.

"Whew!"

"I thought so." Fenton was pleased with his experiment. "You only do it when the last word is easy to rhyme with, Kerby. There aren't any words that *really* rhyme with elephant."

"Well, that's something, at least," said Kerby. "But what am I going to do about those other times when there *are* rhymes? What if I start talking limericks when Mom or Pop says something to me? What if I start doing it at school? They'll worry. They'll take me to the doctor. There's no telling where it will all end!"

"Don't get worked up, Kerby. Maybe it will wear off."

"I hope so."

"If I were you, I'd stay in my room till suppertime, and come straight back up after supper. Tell them you have to do your homework."

"I will." Then Kerby thought of something else, and brightened up a trifle. "Hey, Fenton, you still want to see my poem?"

"I sure do!"

Kerby opened his desk drawer and handed him the notebook. Fenton read the poem through twice without saying anything. When he handed it back, there was a look almost of awe on his face.

"Think it's good?" asked Kerby.

"It's better than good. It's terrific. It's miles ahead of anything I ever read by any boy or even any girl in school anywhere. It can't miss winning," Fenton predicted flatly. "Gee, I'd give anything to write something that good, just once!"

Kerby looked at him dubiously. "Well, there's still plenty of those two chemicals . . ."

"Oh, no! I don't want to do it *that* bad!" cried Fenton with one of his quick grins. "But I sure wish I could do it on my own. Listen, though —I just thought of something. Remember how it was when you tried that lemonade trick? You were all right the next morning."

Kerby's heart lifted like a feather in a breeze.

"Say, that's right! After I'd had a good night's sleep, I was all right."

"Yes . . . until the next time you tried the same trick, that is."

"Well, don't worry about that. There won't be any next time this time!"

The sound of the family car coming up the driveway made his heart flutter.

"There they are! Gee, I hope I don't start talking limericks and get them all worked up."

"Talk as little as you can, stay in your room as much as you can—and go to bed early," was Fenton's advice. "I've got to go home now. I'll see you tomorrow."

Fenton went downstairs, and Kerby heard him saying hello to his parents in his polite way as he went out. When they came in the back door, Kerby called downstairs.

"Hi!"

"Hello, dear," said his mother.

"Hi, Son," said his father.

"Mom, can I work on my homework till supper?"

"Why, certainly, if you want to."

"Such industry!" he heard his father say.

"Well, I'm pretty busy. I'll see you at supper," he told them, and sagged with relief as he closed the door. Just to keep from telling a lie, he did do his homework until he was called. Then he walked downstairs on tingling legs, feeling like someone carrying a time bomb that might go off at any minute.

"Well, Kerby," said his father as they sat down at the table, "anything else new since we saw you last?"

"Nothing much," said Kerby, hoping he didn't look and sound as breathless as he felt.

"What were you working on so hard, dear?"

"Oh, a lot of stuff, Mom."

"Have you written your poem yet?"

"Yes, sort of."

"Good. When do we get to hear it?"

Kerby scrunched down in his chair. He did not want to read them the poem just then and have them wonder how he ever managed to write such a good one. Better to let it come as a surprise later on.

"Well . . . pretty soon. Not yet."

"All right. But we certainly want to hear it when you're ready."

"Okay, Mom."

The thing Kerby most wanted was to have his mother stop talking to him. Every time she opened her mouth he was terrified. What if she said something that started him off?

Fortunately, his father had some things he wanted to tell her about stuff at his office, and Kerby was able to stay out of the conversation until he was pecking away at his dessert. It was chocolate pudding, ordinarily one of his favorites, but tonight he could not seem to get interested in food of any kind.

His mother noticed, of course.

"What's the matter, Kerby? Something wrong with the pudding?"

"Oh, no, Mom. It's swell," said Kerby, beginning to eat faster.

"Here, now, stop that. You don't have to shovel," she said. She leaned forward to inspect him with a mother's worried eye. "Kerby, do you feel all right? You look a little pale to me. And you've been awfully quiet."

"Aw, I'm fine, Mom!"

"Maybe old A. J. Carmody has got him upset," said his father. "That reminds me—I talked to Sid Edwards about him after the wedding, and he claimed the old boy *does* have a good side to him, if you can only get on it. He says he thinks that if you boys are careful not to rub him wrong, Mr. Carmody just might change his mind about your clubhouse. Sid says he's been known to do things like that, contrary to what people think."

If his father had wanted to torture Kerby, he could not have done a better job than he was accidentally doing with the best intentions in the world. As Kerby listened, and thought about how he had made Mr. Carmody their enemy forever, he felt as though every one of his father's words were a knife twisting in his stomach.

"Kerby, you *do* look pale, I don't care what you say!" declared his mother. "I want you to go straight upstairs and get into bed. Some extra sleep is certainly in order."

Kerby sat up straighter.

"Okay, Mom!" he said thankfully—which was, of course, a mistake, and made both his parents look at him with suspicious surprise. His mother reached over and felt his forehead.

"Now I know he's sick," said his father. "When he doesn't gripe about going to bed early, he's a sick boy."

"He doesn't seem to have any fever," said Mrs. Maxwell, even though to Kerby it felt as if the rubbed spot on his forehead were glowing like a brand against her palm. "Well, you get to bed, and we'll see how you are in the morning."

Kerby kissed them good night and headed upstairs. It was all he could do not to run. With Waldo trotting along at his heels, he had reached the door of his room, and was reveling in the feeling of being safe at last after a million narrow escapes, when his mother remembered something.

"Oh, Kerby!" His heart thumped.

"Yes, Mom?"

"What did you do with the glue?"

Bzzzz! With a desperate effort Kerby stepped into his room and shut the door.

"Well, what did you want me to do? I spread it on bread and stood on my head, and ate it and slowly turned blue!" he said.

Then he grabbed the bottle of glue from his desk and yanked the door open again.

"What did you say, Kerby?" his mother was asking.

"I have it up here, Mom!"

"Well, don't shut your door when you're talking to me. I couldn't hear a word you said. Put it out on the hall table, please. I'll get it later."

Kerby did as he was told, then returned to his room and rushed over to his bed. Waldo, settling himself on the small rug beside it, cocked his head up at him, wondering what all the rush was about.

"Whew! Talk about close ones—that was *it*," breathed Kerby. He lay back thankfully on his pillow. "Will I ever be glad when it's morning!"

Chapter Five

Slowly Kerby became aware of gentle pressure on his forehead. Dimly he heard his parents' voices.

"He certainly hasn't any fever," said his mother, taking her hand away.

"Well, let's hope he wakes up feeling fine."

Kerby's sleepiness vanished. It was morning! Would he be all right now? No more limericks? He was glad his mother had only felt his forehead. If she were to listen to his heart, she would call the doctor for sure! He kept his eyes shut, hoping his parents would go away so that he would not have to talk just yet. But then his father gave him his usual call: "Morning, Kerby. Time to get up, Son."

"*Hmmm?*" Kerby pretended to be very sleepy.

"Well, that sounds normal enough," declared his father. "I've got to dress—you get him moving."

Kerby's mother shook him gently.

"Kerby."

"Hmmm?"

"Kerby, wake up. I want to be sure you don't have any problems this morning."

Kerby stirred around, sat up, stretched, and yawned elaborately.

"I'm okay," he said. "I had a good night, and I feel all right."

"Good." His mother hurried toward the door. "I'll get breakfast on the table. Don't be long."

"Don't worry. I'll hurry."

Kerby got up and began to dress for school. As he put on his clothes, he felt vaguely disturbed. Something about the things he had said . . . He glanced at Waldo, who was having his morning stretch.

"Well, anyway, Waldo, I don't feel sick—and I *didn't* say a limerick," he commented, and then froze.

Now he knew what was wrong.

Don't worry. I'll hurry. . . .

I had a good night, and I feel all right. . . .

"Waldo! Every *time*, I make a *rhyme!*"

He sat down hard on his chair.

"It doesn't sound like limericks; but still I'm in an awful fix! Suppose you were under some awful curse that made *you* run around barking verse? You wouldn't like it a bit. Darn it, can't I quit?" cried Kerby, and he was so angry that he slapped the side of his head.

"If I keep this up all day I'll be in a worse fix than ever!" he groaned. Then he blinked at Waldo hopefully. "Hey! At least I didn't do it that time. And I'm still not doing it. I guess hitting myself on the head made it stop. But how long will that last? For Pete's sake, I can't go around hitting myself on the head every time I want to say something!" he declared, because immediately he had an uneasy feeling that his relief was only temporary, and that the rhymes would be back again.

He came down for breakfast as late as he dared so that he would have to eat in a rush, with no time for talking. This worked out so well that he was able to get by with no more than a few one-word or two-word remarks such as "Milk, please" and "Thanks."

"If you don't feel all right, Kerby, have the school call me and I'll come get you."

"Sure, Mom."

"Now run upstairs and brush your teeth."

"Okay."

After giving his teeth one of their less thorough brushings, Kerby grabbed his books and rushed downstairs again.

"Do you have your lunch money?"

"Yes, Mom."

"Have a good day."

"Okay, Mom. G'by."

But when Waldo tried to follow him out, Kerby forgot himself.

"Stay here, Waldo; you know the rule—you mustn't follow me to school," he said sternly.

His mother laughed. "Well, listen to that! You're a poet and don't know it!"

"G'by!" said Kerby again, and hurried out, thinking bitterly that the trouble was he *did* know it.

When he crossed the vacant lot, he was glad to find Fenton waiting for him.

"Bumps went with his father, but I said I'd wait for you. Well, what about it, Kerby? Are you better this morning?"

Kerby shook his head.

"I'm not better, I'm worse! I'm still talking verse. See? I did it then! I did it again!"

"My golly! Is that the latest?"

"Yes. Limericks were bad enough, but what do you call this kind of stuff?"

Fenton cocked his head toward Kerby, listening.

"Let me hear a little more," he urged.

"Aw, lay off!"

"Come on! Say anything."

Kerby could not think of anything to say. He glanced around and saw a Boy Scout poster in a store window. He pointed to it.

"Any Scout can know a tree, but how many talk in poetry?" he asked glumly.

"Hey, that's pretty good, Kerby! You're talking couplets. Couplets are two lines that rhyme."

"Well—whatever they are, they've got to stop. Wait till I give myself a bop," said Kerby, and thumped the side of his head so sharply that Fenton was startled.

"Hey, what are you doing?"

"That stopped it before. Maybe it will stop it this time. . . . There! You see? It did."

"You mean you have to whack yourself on the head to make it stop?"

"Yes."

"Gee, Kerby, you can't keep that up all day."

"You think I don't know it? My ears are ringing right now."

"You'll get punchy!"

"You're telling me! And besides, what will Miss McFee think? And all the kids?"

They walked along for a moment in silence. Then Fenton snapped his fingers.

"I know! Tell her you have a bad case of laryngitis and can't talk."

"What's laryngitis?"

"A sore throat. The kind that makes you lose your voice."

"Say! That's a great idea!"

But as quickly as he had thought of this brilliant scheme, Fenton found a flaw in it.

"No, it's no good. Won't work."

"Why not?"

"You'd have to have a note from home, or she'd never believe you."

"I could have got laryngitis walking to school, couldn't I?" suggested Kerby, who hated to give up such a good idea. But Fenton shook his head.

"Too sudden. She *still* would never believe you. No—I guess you'll just have to hope she doesn't call on you for anything. Be careful in class.

Don't whisper or fool around. Pay attention, but try not to catch her eye. That's all you can do."

Normally, Kerby tended to be talkative. More than once he had gotten in trouble for whispering to his neighbors in class. But not today. Today he was a model pupil. Nobody could get a word out of him. And for a long time Miss McFee did not call on him. He was beginning to hope he might even make it all the way to recess without having to open his mouth once.

"Now, children, we'll spend a few minutes with our natural-history books," said Miss McFee. "Take them out, please."

A murmur of pleasure accompanied the sound of books being opened and pages rustling, because everybody liked the new natural-history book. The class spent a few minutes each day discussing what they had read.

"Now, first let's review some of the animals we have studied so far. Who can tell us something about the kangaroo?"

Hands went up, but not Kerby's. Trying to look as serious and interested as possible, he busily turned pages in his book.

"Irma," said Miss McFee, and Irma Mosley stood up.

"The kangaroo is found in Australia. It is a marsupial—it has a pouch in front to carry its babies in. It has large, strong hind legs for hopping about, and a long thick tail."

"Very good, Irma. Now, who can tell us something about the giraffe?"

Again, as hands went up, Kerby tried to look as if he were paying close attention. But at the same time he was careful not to glance directly at Miss McFee and thus take a chance of catching her eye. To make a good showing, he planned to shoot his hand up the instant she started to call on someone else.

She looked toward the back of the room.

"All right, Jimmie," she began, and Kerby put his hand up.

"No, on second thought—Kerby," she said. "We haven't heard from Kerby this morning."

"Ulp!" Glancing at Fenton, who seemed to be all eyes at that point, Kerby struggled to his feet, hoping for the best.

"I have to laugh when I see a giraffe. He's a physical wreck with a heck of a neck. I can't say much for the way he grew, and I'll say the same for the kangaroo."

Giggles, titters, and guffaws burst forth on all sides, while Kerby's face turned red. It took Miss McFee quite some time to get over her surprise and hold up her hand for order.

"Children, children! Kerby, if I want a funny answer I'll ask for it. I consider you impertinent."

"I'm sorry, Miss McFee. I didn't mean to be."

Miss McFee gasped, suddenly aware of the rhymes and rhythms Kerby was producing. They could be accidental, of course, but . . .

"Now, Kerby. Really tell us something about the giraffe, please."

"How about elephants?" said Kerby desperately, remembering that nothing rhymed with elephants.

"No, Kerby, let's hear something about giraffes," insisted his teacher.

In such a tight spot, there seemed only one thing to do. Quickly Kerby gave himself a whack on the side of his head—and as he did so, the bell rang for recess.

Think It Over

1. Early in the story you learned that Kerby was worried over two things. What were they?
2. Why did Kerby, Fenton, and Bumps not want other members in their club? Do you think this was selfish?
3. What did Mr. Carmody mean when he called the boys' clubhouse an *eyesore*?
4. Do you think Kerby was the kind of boy who was willing to work hard for what he wanted? Give the reasons for your answer.
5. How did Kerby get his chemistry set? How did he feel whenever he used it? Why did he feel as he did?
6. What is a limerick?
7. What did Kerby do to annoy Mr. Carmody at their second meeting?
8. Give as many words as you can think of to describe how Kerby felt after this meeting.
9. Do you think that the poem could really be considered Kerby's own poem? Why do you think as you do?
10. What are some things you hope to find out if you can get the book and read the rest of it?

Discovering New Words

Write the meaning of each underlined word in the sentences below. You may turn back to the page numbers shown and read the paragraph before and after the sentences. Check your answers with the dictionary.

1. Mr. Maxwell sat down on the side of the bed, staring at Kerby with incredulous eyes. (page 24)
2. Bumps was sizing up Kerby's nose with an ominous gleam in his eye. (pages 48-49)
3. Fenton was concentrating hard. (page 57)
4. "Kerby, if I want a funny answer I'll ask for it. I consider you impertinent." (page 76)

Going Beyond the Book

1. Now that you have read the first part of *The Limerick Trick*, you will want to get the book to find out how the story ends. But before you do this, try to write your own ending for the story.
2. See if you can write one or two limericks as amusing as Kerby's limericks.

More Books to Read

CARROLL, RUTH and LATROBE. *Beanie.**
New York: Henry Z. Walck, Inc., 1953.

Beanie lives on a farm in the Great Smoky Mountains. When he gets a make-believe gun and a new puppy for his birthday, he decides the time has come to go on a bear hunt. But he never expects to meet a real bear!

CONE, MOLLY. *Mishmash.*
Boston: Houghton Mifflin Company, 1962.

When you're a new boy in town, it helps to have a dog. And Mishmash is just the dog to make a boy well known by everyone.

ESTES, ELEANOR. *Ginger Pye.*
New York: Harcourt, Brace & World, Inc., 1951.

When a new puppy joins the Pye family, he is named Ginger Pye. The family and he are all very happy together until the awful Thanksgiving Day when Ginger Pye is kidnaped.

TAYLOR, SYDNEY. *All-of-a-Kind Family.*
Chicago: Follett Publishing Company, 1951.

The All-of-a-Kind Family have little money but are rich in love and friendship. Five girls and their mother keep happy and busy.

*Included in *Invitations to Personal Reading,* Curriculum Foundation Classroom Library, Scott, Foresman and Company.

Marguerite de Angeli is the author and also the illustrator of many books. She has a great interest in people who were born in another country but who came many years ago to live in our country. She is especially interested in those who came to the part of Pennsylvania where she makes her home, and the way they lived is often the subject matter for her stories.

Although she planned to be a concert singer when she grew up, Miss de Angeli chose instead to marry and to raise a family. Very soon she began writing books for young readers. Her own five children and later her grandchildren became models for the characters she created. Among her best-known books are *The Door in the Wall, Yonie Wondernose,* and *Thee, Hannah!*

Skippack School

Marguerite de Angeli

It had been a very long journey for
Eli Shrawder and his family. From
Germany they had crossed the ocean
to America. Now they had finally come
to a little Mennonite settlement on
Skippack Creek in Pennsylvania. It
was exciting to start life over again
in a new country. Although America
was different from Germany, in many
ways Eli liked his new home and the
friends he quickly made. As you
read this book, you will enjoy finding
out about life in this pioneer
community.

Skippack School

JESU MEIN LICHT

Being the story of
Eli Shrawder
and of one
Christopher Dock, schoolmaster
about the year 1750
By
Marguerite de Angeli
Doubleday and Company, Inc.

To My
Mother

Here is the way to say some of the words used in this book.

Amos Freyer (ā′məs frī′ər)
Anneke (än′ə kə)
Barbara Ann (bär′bə rə an)
Bethlehem (beth′lē əm)
Casper Weimar (kas′pər wī′mär)
Catherine Shrawder (kath′ər in shrô′dər)
Christopher Dock (kris′tə fər dok)
Christopher Sauer (kris′tə fər sou′ər)
Claus Johnson (klôs jon′sn)
Eli (ē′lī)
Eliza (i lī′zə)
Fraktur-Schriften (fräk túr′ shrif′tən)
Gabriel (gā′brē əl)
German Town (jėr′mən toun)
Gerrit Inden Hoffen (ger′it in′dən hôf′ən)
Grumblethorpe (grum′bl thôrp)
Jacob Heebner (jā′kəb hēb′nər)
Jonas Eidmuller (jō′nəs īd′mul ər)
Katie Kreider (kā′tē krī′dər)
Lenni Lenape (len′ē len′ə pē)
Margareth (mär′gə rət)
Mennonites (men′ən īts)
Pennsylvania (pen′sl vā′nē ə)
Philadelphia (fil′ə del′fē ə)
Reuben (rü′bən)
Rittenhouse (rit′n hous)
Shackamaxon (shak′əmaks′ən)
Sibilla (si bil′ə)
Skeback (skē′bak)
Skippack (skip′ak)
Tobias Bean (tō bī′əs bēn)
William Penn (wil′yəm pen)
Wissahickon (wis′ə hik′ən)

You may need to use the pronunciation key in the glossary in *Roads to Follow*, or in the *Thorndike-Barnhart Beginning Dictionary*.

85

REE-EE-K! CREE-EE-K!" The wheels of the cart groaned and squeaked as they turned round and round over the block pavement on High Street in Philadelphia. They went up past the Court House, then turned off onto the road that led out into Penn's Woods and through the German Town.

To Eli it seemed as if he could still feel the roll of the ship beneath him. He and his father and mother, Peter and Catherine Shrawder, and his two little sisters had landed early that morning. They had crossed the ocean in the ship called *The Charming Nancy* and had been ten long weeks on the ocean. Eli shivered as he remembered the storm at sea that made them all ill, and the terror that came over him when giant waves rolled the boat, and the chests and boxes slid from one side to the other of the cabin floor.

He was glad to be on land, with the fresh country air to sniff. It was good! The wagon creaked on and on, out through the deep woods.

"It wonders me now," said Pop, "that the houses stand so close in Penn's green country town."

"Yah," said Mom, "like a city it vas, but *here* iss nice!"

Cousin Jacob called back to them.

"Soon now," he said, "we come to the German Town." Cousin Jacob rode ahead on horseback. He and Cousin Hannah had lived in the German Town for several years, and he had come down to meet the ship and help Pop buy a wagon to take them and their few pieces of furniture to the land out in the newer settlement beyond the German Town. Buck and Berry, the oxen, and Star, the cow, had come with them across the ocean.

"Over there by the Wissahickon Creek iss Rittenhouse's paper mill. Good paper he makes." Cousin Jacob pointed to his left. Eli had never seen a paper mill. It sounded exciting. He wished he could see it, but he could find no sign of the mill through the thick woods, only the trail leading toward it.

Slowly the wagon creaked over the deep ruts in the road. Oxen always move slowly, and besides, Star, the cow, was tethered to the back of the cart; but by noon they got to the German Town, and there was Cousin Hannah to greet them. She came out the gate and helped them to climb down from the wagon—Sibilla, then Eli, then Mom. "Ach!" she said in German, "so tired you must be! And the *little* one." She took the tiny babe from Mom and led them into the house.

After a bountiful dinner in Cousin Jacob's fine house, they set out again in the wagon. Cousin Hannah tucked in a basket filled with good things. She had a box of live geese ready, too. They tied it on the back of the wagon.

"Something, now, to begin with," she said. And she and Cousin Jacob stood at the gate and waved good-by as they started off.

It was market day, and the street was filled with people on horseback and afoot. The sides of the street were lined with wagons and with food stalls. Eli even saw two or three of the Indians he had heard about. Cousin Jacob had said they were all friendly because William Penn had treated them with such fairness. Eli longed to see them better, but Pop wouldn't stop. He was eager to get to their land.

The afternoon wore on. Cree-ee-k! Cree-ee-k! went the wagon wheels. It seemed to Eli as if he had heard that squeaking, grinding noise for weeks.

"Is it soon, Pop, that we come to the place?" he asked.

"Yah, soon," said Pop as they passed a little church that stood away up on the hill. "This is the wide marsh, where the other road comes in. Skeback, or Skippack, or some such, Jacob said. It wonders me if we get there by nightfall."

"It gives a long journey," said Mom, and sighed. Then she took a deep breath. "It gives a good smell, too, and room for growing, ain't?"

Eli sat between Pop and Mom. Sibilla, his little sister, who was four, sat on Mom's lap. The baby, Barbara Ann, was asleep in her cradle in the back of the cart. She had been born aboard ship coming across the Atlantic Ocean from Holland, where they had waited so long for word about the land Pop had bought from Cousin Jacob.

The Shrawders and many other families had left Germany together to find new homes where they could worship God in their own way. They called themselves Mennonites after their leader, Menno Simons. They dressed "plain" like the English Friends who had already come to Pennsylvania. The men even had hooks and eyes to fasten their vests instead of buttons. The women wore plain dark dresses and white kerchiefs and caps. They had gone first to Holland, where they stayed for a time; but there they heard such glowing reports of the new land in America from Cousin Jacob and others who had settled in Penn's Woods that they had set out to find it.

"So to Pennsylvanie, then, we shall go," said Pop one day. But it had been many months before they could get passage on a boat to the New World. Already the home life in Germany was so far away that it seemed like a dream. Pop said there were many Germans along the Skippack Creek in Pennsylvania near where they were going and in the village called Skippack, so it would be a little like home.

Now they were almost there. Eli looked up through the great trees, so much like the ones he remembered in Germany. The woods were full of the songs of birds; squirrels and small animals of all kinds crossed the wagon trail, and the land seemed full of plenty.

They had passed few houses since leaving the German Town, but finally they came to a tavern. Pop said, "Now we are near to our land. Here we stay for the night."

Mom, the baby, and Sibilla had a great double bed in one of the rooms of the Swan Tavern kept by Gerrit Inden Hoffen, but Pop made a place in the wagon and said to Eli, "We can sleep here and save the cost of another room."

Early the next morning they set out again. Smoke was just beginning to rise from the chimneys of the few farmhouses they passed. But by the time they reached the village store it was open, and a little boy was sweeping off the steps.

He stared curiously at the wagon, then ran inside and they heard him calling, "Oh, Pop, the new neighbors it must be."

The storekeeper hurried out to greet them, smiling a welcome.

"Yah, Jacob was right. He sent word last week only that he was sure your ship would be in within a few days. And a good time it is, too, for the building. The spring planting is finished; everyone will be ready to start today."

Cousin Jacob had told Pop that it was the custom in Penn's Woods for the neighbors to gather and help cut the trees and build the cabin whenever new settlers arrived. And now the storekeeper was explaining that he would send word to all the farmers.

"Right ahead you go, into the woods past the Eidmuller farm," he directed. "Nice land you have, and soon a new home. We start with the building today."

The woods were still cool when they passed the great butternut tree that marked the corner of their land. Eli had been watching for the tree. It was shown on the map of the land Cousin Jacob had given Pop.

He shouted with excitement when he saw it— but Pop didn't stop. They drove on more slowly until they found a slight clearing in the woods.

"This makes a good home place," Pop said. Mom nodded agreement, and Eli and Sibby jumped off the wagon and ran happily through the woods, glad to be once more on land.

Pop had hardly picked out the spot for the house before the first farmer arrived. It was Jonas Eidmuller, whose farm bordered the Shrawders' land.

"Soon, now, the others will come," he said. "To set the posts for the house *now* vas *gut!* The moon stands up *so* and dey vill shtay." He held up his two forefingers to show how the moon stood.

Eli knew the old belief among the Germans that fence posts or buildings must be set in the ground only when the crescent moon was on its back, or the ground would be soggy and the posts would not be solid.

"Und soon now is the time for planting beans," Jonas Eidmüller continued. "Nex' week iss gut. It iss de sign of the twins in de almanac. You plant den, and dey grow *plenty* und *big,* too!"

One by one the farmers came, some in wagons, some afoot. Their wives came, too, and each family had food for themselves and to spare. They brought great kettles and put them up with chains on three poles set together.

While the men chopped down trees, the women cooked. They cooked food Eli had never tasted before. Corn meal, scrapple, and pepper pot. The babies were put to sleep in the wagons, and the young children, who didn't go to school, gathered small wood for the fires and played with the babies when they waked. It was like a festival, Eli thought. When school was over, some of the older children came to watch and to be with their parents.

Everyone worked hard. A sharp ax and good strong muscles were needed to chop down the big trees, but they were so large that it didn't take a great many to build the house. There were stones in a nearby quarry to use for the chimney and springs of clear water close at hand. No wonder the reports of Penn's Woods had traveled so far!

Eli was allowed to trim off some of the branches as the trees came down, and he felt it was much more fun than anything he had ever done.

After the branches were cut off, each log was trimmed with the adz and cut at the ends to fit so that there wouldn't be too much space between them to be chinked with mud. When night came, some of the farmers and their families went home, and some slept in the wagons.

The next day everyone was up early. Eli fed the animals. Then Pop told him to go help Jonas Eidmuller split shingles for the roof.

"Yah, sure you can help," Jonas said. "In piles by the walls they should go, so it makes easier when they start the roofing. That's a good boy."

Eli made many trips with the shingles; and in between times he rested a bit and listened to Jonas Eidmuller, who was a great talker.

"So," he said, "you like this new home, yes?" Eli nodded.

"And soon," Jonas continued, "you will be off to school with the other young ones. That you will like, too, eh? Master Christopher Dock makes a fine school here on the Skippack."

This time Eli didn't nod. School was the one thing he didn't like about this new home. He had gone to school only a few months in Germany— and he had hated being shut in. He hadn't learned much either—not even all of his letters—because he didn't pay attention. The schoolmaster was cross and had even sent a note home, complaining of his mischief and lack of attention.

Mom had worried about it. On the ship she had tried teaching Eli his letters, but there were always interruptions. She had told Eli he must do better in the new home. And Eli had promised to be good and work hard—but he still wasn't happy about school.

By the third night the roof of the new cabin was on. All the farmers and their families went back to their homes, and Pop and Eli moved in the furniture they had brought across the ocean. Mom was as pleased as she could be with the wide

fireplace, its iron crane for pots and kettles, and the oven at one end. The floor, made of short pieces of log set on end, formed a pattern of circles. It smelled clean and fresh, and it was solid to step upon.

Next day, Mom's and Pop's bed was built into a corner of the room, and the curtains brought from the homeland were put up. Eli's bed, made of stout pine logs with the bark peeled off, was set up in the loft. Sibilla's trundle bed was there, too, and Eli cut fresh pine branches to put under the feather ticks. Sibilla brought her little play cupboard and chair and put them in the chimney corner. Pop set the clock between the windows, and Mom put the spinning wheel close by.

"It makes not much furniture," said Mom as she hung the house blessing over the front door.

"Ach," said Pop as he moved the painted chest against the far wall, "soon we make more! Some wide boards iss left from the door-making, und Eli helps good with a saw and plane. We soon make a table and other things. Eli, here, thinks he can make a bench for you to put in front of the fireplace. Already, a good board he has found."

There was much laughing and happy talk as they put the wash bench by the back door, and Mom hung up her pots and kettles by the fireplace. Then Pop laid the fire for supper. *It was home!*

OR A WEEK, Eli helped Pop clear the space around the house and set things in order. They made a table and built a small shelter for the cattle and fixed a workbench and a place for Pop's tools. And, whenever he had a minute, Eli worked on the fireplace bench. It was a good piece of pine, Pop said, and not to be wasted. He showed Eli how to use the plane to smooth it and helped him make the holes for the end pieces.

Eli worked carefully—but he could hardly wait to get the thick board smooth enough so he could begin on the carving. It was to have a carved border, as nearly like the one on a little bench Mom's brother had made for her, in Germany, as

Eli could make it. Mom had hated to leave the bench, but they could not bring everything they wanted so far across the ocean.

Eli remembered every detail of the border. And he loved to carve. He had his own knife, one his uncle had given him so he shouldn't forget his wood carving in Penn's Woods. But for the bench Pop said he would have to use the small chisel.

Mom was pleased about the bench, too. Eli hoped that she would forget about school until he had finished it. But when Sunday came, she said firmly, "Now to school you must go."

The next morning Pop took Eli to the bend in the road and told him to follow the path. It would lead him to the schoolhouse that stood beside the log Mennonite Church where several trails met.

Eli stopped to shy a stone at a scampering woodchuck. He missed it. Mr. Woodchuck scuttled under the leaves of an oak seedling; then he was gone. Eli looked and looked but couldn't find where. He picked up his lunch basket and went on his way to school. . . . School! How he dreaded to go to school in this new place! It was so much more fun to chase squirrels in the woods or go fishing or work on Mom's bench.

He dragged his feet through cool leaves and grass, looked up through the tall trees, and wished he could stay at home, even if it meant working in the fields or chopping wood for Mom; yes, even if it meant minding the baby in her cradle! *Anything* would be better than going to this new school! "Probably," he thought, "the schoolmaster will be ugly and cross."

Eli heard the bell ringing and began to run. In just a moment the trees thinned a bit, and he came out in a little clearing. There stood the school and the church just as Pop had said. The boys and girls were all going in, but instead of pushing and crowding as Eli remembered their doing in the other school, they were walking in two by two, the boys waiting until last. He hurried a little faster in order not to be late; he didn't want a caning the very first day!

He came up to the door as the last two boys were going in. Just then the schoolmaster came to the door.

"Come, come, boys! What is keeping you?" he asked. Then he spied Eli. "So," he said, "a new *boy* we have! Come in, sir." He took Eli by the hand and led him to the front of the room.

"It wonders me what he is going to do to me!" Eli thought. His heart beat fast. He saw two or three children who had been to the log raising, Amos and Reuben and a little girl named Anneke —but still he felt strange.

"Now," said the schoolmaster, "I am Master Christopher Dock, and these are all your friends. Will you tell us your name?"

Eli's throat was very dry, but he managed to say, "Eli Shrawder, sir."

"Eli Shrawder! Then you are the boy who lives in that new house. Boys and girls, stand up and greet Eli!" They all stood up, and the boys made bows and the girls curtsied.

"Now," said Master Christopher, "you may sit there on the bench beside Amos Freyer. Make room for him, Amos." Eli sat down on the bench. The desks and benches were around the walls, facing outward; the boys sat on one side of the room, the girls on the other. The schoolmaster sat at a desk on the little platform at the front of the room. On the desk were inkstand, sandbox, and quill pen; several books beside the Bible; and some field flowers in a vase. Eli saw that the schoolmaster had a birch rod up on the pegs at one side

where it was handy, and on the other side, a rifle in its rack. It was warm enough for the windows to be open, so there was no need for a fire in the ten-plate stove that stood in the middle of the room. All the children were neat and clean, Eli noticed, and when Master Christopher spoke to them, they were very respectful.

"Eli Shrawder," said the master when the first class went to the platform, "do you know your letters?"

"Some," said Eli.

"Eli, when you speak to me, say, 'Yes, Master Christopher.' That is the proper way to answer any man, not because especial respect is due *me*."

This time Eli said, "Yes, Master Christopher, I know some of the letters." Then he had to take the pointer and point out what he knew. He was a little ashamed that he didn't know more when Master Christopher said, "Amos, you take care to see that Eli learns his letters; then he can stand with the first class."

"Yes, Master Christopher," said Amos. The lessons went on. Amos, talking quietly, told Eli how the master helped the children to do their best; how he often gave them presents for good work —pictures and verses called "Fraktur-Schriften," because that meant picture writing. Amos said when they learned to write well, they were allowed sometimes to write letters to the children in the German Town School and receive letters in return. Master Christopher carried the letters back and forth. He taught the first half of the week in the Skippack School and the other half in the German Town School. So Wednesday afternoons were saved for special exercises, for spelling bees, and for the giving of prizes.

When noontime came, Master Christopher said, "Now, Eliza, and you, Tobias Bean, shall have each a sugar pretzel; you have learned well today. Jacob, for your excellent attention this morning, you may read the chapter from the Old Testament while the children are eating.

"Read where it says, 'Train up a child in the way he should go and when he is old, he will not depart from it.' School is dismissed for dinner."

He struck a little bell, and the children formed two lines as they had done coming in. They filed out quietly but burst into laughter and talk for a few moments until Jacob, perched on a tree stump, began to read. Then they sat down on the grass and ate quietly.

Eli, who thought this a very tame way to spend the free time between morning and afternoon lessons, began to shy stones up into the trees. It was all very well till one of them fell on the roof; then Master Christopher came to the door. He took off his glasses and looked at all the children; then seeing Eli standing and the others sitting, he said, "Eli Shrawder, were you throwing stones?"

Eli looked into the master's eyes and said, "Yes, Master Christopher, but I didn't hurt anybody."

"No, but you *might,* and you might break the windows. That wouldn't do at all. Windows cost a great deal of money." Eli knew that, because Pop had said they would have to use oiled paper for the windows at home for a while. He said, "Yes, Master Christopher," and his face was very red because all the children were looking at him.

The afternoon went better. Eli knew the verses that had to be recited because Mom had taught them to him. He still couldn't tell many of the letters, but Master Christopher said, "There is time for all, my boy, if only we do not waste it. If today you do not learn, but *try,* the next time it will go better."

Claus Johnson whispered to Eli. "Sometimes," he said, "Master Christopher lets me help make pencils, and sometimes he takes a boy to visit the German Town School. But never have I been."

Claus whispered so often that he was made to sit on the dunce's stool the rest of the afternoon.

Finally the master looked at his big silver watch.

"Now, Claus," he said at last, "can you be quiet tomorrow? Today you made Eli talk, too. School is for learning. Do not forget! Jacob, remember to ask your mother to sew up the rent in your shirt.

Sarah, dear child, see if you can read well tomorrow, and remember not to twist your hair."

"Yes, Master Christopher," said Sarah, "but my hair is so stribbly."

"Reuben," said the master as he leaned over a boy near him, "if you do well at reading this week, you will be glad when Wednesday comes.

"Now God bless you all and bring you back safe in the morning."

The girls got up and walked out two by two; then the boys followed.

Eli could scarcely believe it. A *whole* day and not once had the schoolmaster used the birch rod! Not once had he even been angry! It ought to be easy to have fun in this school. Eli tossed his broad hat into the air.

VERY DAY after school, Eli helped Pop to hoe the beans they had planted. He had to keep the woodbox filled, too, and to help care for Star and the oxen. But if he hurried, there was some time every day when he could work on the fireplace bench. He had the boards all planed now and had begun to fit the end pieces into the top.

Several days when Master Christopher was teaching in the German Town and there was no school on the Skippack, Eli went with Pop to help hoe the flax in Jonas Eidmuller's field. Jonas had agreed to share his crop of flax with Pop if they would help work it. Then Mom would have linen to spin into yarn and to make into cloth for shirts and dresses.

At first Eli's arms ached from the hard work, but as the weeks passed, he became used to it and was proud of his muscles. Sometimes Pop let him go fishing with Amos and Claus in the branch that flowed through the village and into the Skippack Creek. Sometimes they slipped off their clothes and went into the water down below the mill race. It felt so cool and good!

Pop worked very hard at clearing the land so that he could plant more the next year. Eli liked that kind of work—trimming branches from trees, burning brush, guiding Buck and Berry as they dragged the stumps from the ground. The small animals they discovered as they worked supplied food for the table. Sometimes they caught wild turkeys that Mom roasted on the spit.

Mom did the milking and made the butter and cheese. She said a little rhyme as she worked the butter. It went like this:

> *Come, butter, come,*
> *Come, butter, come,*
> *Peter's waiting at the gate,*
> *Waiting for a buttered cake,*
> *Come, butter, come.*

Mom had to dip candles, too, and do the spinning and knitting. While she was busy, Sibilla played with the baby in her cradle or on a quilt under a tree.

Mom had set cabbages out in part of the space Pop cleared first so that she could make sauerkraut for winter. Corn meal, which they had learned to like so well, and wheaten flour they could get at Gerrit Inden Hoffen's mill. To be sure, Pop didn't have any money left after all their journeying, but Mom had things in the painted chest that could be traded. She had steel needles, which were very scarce in the new land, and medicines given her by her father, who was an apothecary in Germany. Mom also had bolts of flowered silks from her wedding dowry, and these could be traded for necessities now that she and Pop had joined the "plain" people, the Mennonites.

School kept on through the summer, because in midwinter when the roads were impassable, it had to be closed.

Slowly Eli learned the capitals and small letters, but it was hard not to get them mixed. Sometimes he wondered if he could possibly learn them before school closed. It was so hard to keep his mind on letters. He sat right in front of the window, and there was always something to watch outside. The bluejays were always fighting and squawking, their blue wings flashing in and out of the leaves. A family of gray squirrels raced up and down the oak tree down by the spring. Once a fox came out of the woods and stood for a moment gazing toward the schoolhouse. Eli was so surprised that he stood up and stared out the window. Just then Master Christopher called on him to join the children who were going up to recite their A B C's. He had to be spoken to twice.

"Eli Shrawder," said the master, "the Book says, 'Love and not sleep, lest thou come to poverty.'"

"But I was not asleep, Master Christopher," said Eli. "I was just wishing I could be out in the woods instead of having letters to learn."

"Your mind was asleep, my boy. How will you

ever learn to read if you never keep your mind on your work?" The master looked sorrowful. "Whatever you want to do, you will find it useful to know your letters and sums."

Many times a week the master had to speak to Eli. He was either thinking up mischief or dreaming about the bench he was making at home. He had the bench together now, and it was all finished except the carving.

June passed and July came in, hot and sultry. It was almost closing time of the last school day of the week, Wednesday. Eli sat trying to puzzle out a sum of numbers. Slate pencils scratched; the droning voices of the girls learning their verses and the bench creaking when the boys wriggled added to his discomfort. The pegs holding up the bench seemed loose. Eli whispered to Amos Freyer; Amos turned and whispered something to Claus Johnson; Claus turned and whispered something to Jacob Heebner; Jacob sniggered. The master was busy with a class of girls at the board. All of a sudden there was a great clatter and crash! Master Christopher looked around in amazement. There on the floor, laughing so hard they couldn't get up, were all the boys from one form. They had wiggled at the legs of the bench till they had all come loose and down clattered bench, boys, and all. Teacher looked grave.

"Now," he said very quietly, "since you boys are so anxious to take wood apart, you shall all stay one hour after school is over and work at the wood-pile. Those logs beside the oak you shall saw and split and pile against the time we shall need them for the stove. Now put the bench together again."

Because the master was so gentle, Eli was ashamed. He almost wished he would use the birch rod instead, as he had that one time when Abel Larsen had cut his name in the desk, then lied about it.

July passed with still, hot days to make the corn grow, and thundershowers to freshen the air. August came in, and the days grew warmer and warmer. It was hard to stay in school and try to learn to read when the flies buzzed and the heat shimmered across the fields, especially when the Skippack Creek ran clear and cool not over half an hour's walk away. Eli could feel just how soft the grass would be along the bank and kept thinking how much fun it was to make whistles of the willow shoots, or to whittle the soft white pine that grew thick in the hollows. School seemed endless and to learn letters or anything else all foolishness.

At noontime, the master gave the children some free time to play. Amos said to Eli, "Let's play 'Eckball,'" corner ball. He showed Eli the new ball he had made of string wound tight and covered with horsehide from the tannery. He told him how to stand at the corner of the building and throw the ball across the roof to the other corner where Amos would be standing. It went over high and well above the roof the first few times. Then Eli tried to make it go higher.

He put all the strength he had into his arm. He must have turned his arm a little because, instead of going over the roof, the ball went *right straight through the window!* Master Christopher rushed out to see who had thrown the ball. He made both Amos and Eli come in, and he kept the ball.

"Now," he said, "your fathers will have to see to replacing the window. 'A foolish son is a grief to his father,' so says the Book." Eli was so scared he had a queer feeling in his stomach.

When closing time came, the master called out the names of several boys and girls. "Eliza, Anneke, Tobias, Jacob, come forward. Eli Shrawder, you may come, too, though you were in that mischief." They all went up to the front of the room.

Eli was sure he would be caned this time. He waited till the master spoke to each of the others.

"Eliza," he said, "you have entered the reading class. You have done well. I give you this gift." Eliza took from him the paper and smiled with pleasure. The paper had on it a painting of a bird set on a heart in which was written, "Noble Heart bethink thine end."

To Anneke the master gave one of the flower paintings and said, "Dear child, so well you are learning to write, soon you may write a letter to Esther in the German Town, and I shall carry it to her."

Eli looked longingly at Anneke's flower painting. How proud Mom would be if he earned one! Every week since he had started school he had

wanted one. But it was only for good work that Master Christopher awarded them—and now, Eli thought sadly, Master Christopher would never give one to anyone who had broken a window.

"Now, Eli, you know," said Master Christopher, "when you have thoroughly learned your small letters, your father owes you a penny and your mother shall cook for you two fried eggs, as I have told them is my custom. You have earned this, but you have also made a great deal of mischief. So, I shall send a note with you to your father that it is time for the penny and the two fried eggs, but he shall be told also about the broken window. And from now on I shall put you in charge of Tobias, who has done well this week. We shall see if he can help you remember that school is not the place for pranks."

Eli was ashamed to be spoken to before the whole class. But he was more ashamed to have to tell Mom and Pop about the window. What would they say? Would Pop punish him?

It was time for dismissal. The master blessed them and sent them home.

Eli walked as far as the top of the hill with Claus, then went slowly on home. He dreaded to tell about the window. As soon as he reached home, he went straight to the shed and began to work at the carving on the bench. The scalloped edge was fun to make and kept him busy till Mom called him to bring in the cow.

HAT EVENING after supper was over, Mom was putting Barbara Ann in her cradle, Pop was feeding the oxen, Sibilla was sitting on the doorstep, and Eli was trying to get the pigs into the shed for the night. He was gathering acorns to coax them in. There was a sound of hoofs, and out of the woods an Indian came riding. Eli was so surprised that he dropped the acorns and ran for the house. The pigs ran, too, and the geese, waddling up from the creek, went squawking in all directions. The Indian saluted Pop, who was coming out of the barn, but he didn't stop. He kept on toward the west and was soon lost in the woods again. It was the first time Eli had seen an Indian that close.

"It wonders me," said Pop, "what it makes that an Indian goes by alone and didn't stop to eat. Ach! Vell, Jacob says they make no trouble here. *So!*" He went to get the grinder he was making and called to Eli to find the pigs again.

"Now come, Eli," he called when the pigs and geese were put in the shed, "and let me see how good you can make the capital letters. Right here in the ground where the earth iss hard, you can make them with a stick." Mom came out with her knitting, and they worked in the evening light.

"Now," thought Eli, "I shall *have* to tell about the window." He stood first on one foot, then the other, and made no attempt to begin on the letters.

"What makes," said Pop, "that you stand and wiggle so?" He looked into Eli's face.

"Ach *so!*" he said. "I see by your eyes that somesing makes wrong. What iss it?"

Then Eli gave Pop the master's note and told him about playing corner ball with Amos and how, without meaning to, he had thrown the ball right through the window.

"Tch, tch!" said Pop. "Now what shall be done? Windows cost money, and you should know to be careful." He sat and thought. Mom dropped her

knitting and said, "The painted chest might have something we could sell, maybe."

"*Eli* should have to pay," said Pop. "He ought to learn to be careful. That bench, now, that he makes, nobody here would buy it, but maybe in the German Town it would sell. Amos he should help, too."

"Oh, no," cried Eli, "the bench, it is for Mom" —and then he stopped. Mom looked sorry, but Pop was shaking his head firmly.

"Yes, the bench I could trade, maybe. When it is finished, I will try in the German Town."

Eli was miserable. To trade Mom's bench for glass! Oh, why had he ever thrown that ball? For the rest of the week he couldn't even work on the bench, he was so disappointed. But on Monday it did help to tell Master Christopher what Pop had said.

"Yes, that is good, my child; perhaps you can sell the bench before the cold weather comes," the master told him. "You and Amos may help me this noontime to put paper over the broken place until we can mend it."

That day Eli tried so hard and made his letters so well that Master Christopher said, "Eli, today

you may stay and help me make lead pencils."
Eli was delighted. They heated lead on the little
stove, then poured it into the cracks of the floor.
When it was cool, they dug it out with a knife,
and the hard lead made good clear marks on paper.
The schoolmaster noticed how interested Eli was
in making things.

"I can see thee likes to use thy hands, Eli," he
said, "but to know the letters and the sums is good,
too, and needful. Keep trying hard, dear child,
and keep thyself from mischief. The Book says,
'He that keepeth himself, is greater than he that
taketh a city.'"

Eli did try hard, but, always, something seemed
to happen. At home he could work steadily for
hours, carving the fireplace bench. In school he
just couldn't keep his mind on lessons, and then
he got into mischief. If the tiny children sat on
the low bench near him, he couldn't seem to help
pinching little Nancy's fat neck and making her
cry, or pulling Catherine's curls from under her
cap.

Master Christopher kept him after school again
and talked to him a long time. Eli promised to
keep from mischief, and he really meant to, but

only a few days later when they were singing the morning hymn, he thought of a play rhyme he remembered from Germany, and he went on singing the rhyme instead of the hymn. The rhyme was funny and made him laugh, so that he had to stop singing altogether. The master only said, " 'A word fitly spoken is like apples of gold in pictures of silver.' Begin the hymn again."

At recess, Amos showed Eli a fan he had made by soaking a piece of soft pine and splitting it in thin blades partway down, then spreading the pieces in fan shape. Eli was supposed to be learning the verse put up before him on the wall, but instead he had been thinking of the scalloped edge he was carving on the bench, and how nice it looked. Now the idea occurred to him that he could make a fan for Mom. It would be something in place of the bench. The fan would be pretty, too, with a pattern cut across the sticks.

"Mom would like a fan like that," he thought. He took his knife out of his pocket and a stick that he kept for whittling, just to try and see how it looked. He cut little notches to form a diamond pattern and was just about to carve a design on the other side when the master called to him.

"Eli, is it that you know so much that you have time for play? 'Folly is joy to him that is destitute of wisdom.' Your exercise must be well learned, so you may stand for questioning."

"Yes, Master Christopher," said Eli, getting to his feet, but he trembled because he didn't know the verse. He was sure Master Christopher would cane him this time!

"Eli," said the master, "what is the verse you have had before you all morning?" All the girls and boys turned in their seats to look at him, and the master took off his spectacles and looked severe.

Eli tried and tried to think what was on the paper that had been hanging before him on the wall, but not a word would come to him. He hung his head.

"Aren't you ashamed?" said the teacher. "Now you are to listen with care and know this before the hour to go home. Jacob, let us hear the exercise." Master Christopher put on his spectacles again and folded his hands behind him.

Jacob was able to say the exercise with only one mistake. Then Sarah was asked to say it. She knew it perfectly but rattled it off too quickly.

Master was very patient. He corrected each one, then gave Eli one more chance to say the verse. Eli knew some of it, but he hadn't learned it perfectly, so he was made to stay after the others had gone and study until he knew every word. Then Master Christopher said he might go. Eli was so glad to be free that he was almost home before he remembered his lunch basket. He had to go back for it and he hurried, hoping the master hadn't left and locked the door. Knowing Master Christopher's habit of study and prayer after the children had gone, Eli went softly over the door-step and lifted the latch carefully.

There was Master Christopher on his knees, his eyes closed and praying aloud.

"And Eli Shrawder, O Lord, he is not a *bad* boy, but he is so full of mischief. Help me to show him how to use his time aright. He has a sweet singing voice, too, but thou knowest that sometimes he uses that voice to say mischief——"

Eli didn't wait to hear any more. He tiptoed out and left his basket. Something rose up in his throat and almost choked him. He ran into the woods and threw himself down. "I must be very wicked," he thought to himself. Then he was afraid someone, perhaps the master, might see him, so he got up, rubbed his eyes, and ran for home. He *would* stop making mischief! He *would* earn one of those bird paintings for Mom.

LL THROUGH the rest of the summer and through September, Eli tried very hard to keep his mind on his school work, and Master Christopher seemed pleased about it.

One evening after supper, Eli asked Mom to hear him read. She wondered why he was suddenly taking so much interest in reading, but she said nothing and just helped him over the hard words. Pop came in from the barn and heard him.

"Yah!" he said. "Good! Good! The little one has learned pat-a-cake, Sibby learns to knit, and *you,* now, *can read!* Tomorrow you can read the Book, for morning prayers."

Pop always read the Scriptures. Eli was very proud. Now, perhaps, Master Christopher would let him read the Scriptures in school. If he did it well, the master would surely give him a present of a flower or bird picture.

The next morning, Eli read the Psalm as Pop had promised. Pop had to help him a little, but he did it very well. He hurried to school as soon as breakfast was over, and that day the lesson went so smoothly for him that the teacher said, "Now, my child, tomorrow you will be able to read the morning Scriptures. You are doing well, Eli. But the Book says, 'Boast not thyself of tomorrow; for thou knowest not what a day may bring forth.'"

Eli knew how glad Mom would be. He could hardly wait to tell her. He wanted to get home and work a little more on the bench before he began the afternoon chores. The carving was done and ready for finishing with the pumice rubbing stone.

Now that the flax was gathered, Eli had to work every afternoon at the flax brake. It was a large double frame of wood, hinged at the back. The stalks of flax were laid between the top and bottom frames; then when the top came down, it broke away the woody stems and left the soft part. After the flax was hackled and combed, Mom heaped it on the spindle for spinning into yarn. Already, much of it was done, and Mom kept the spinning wheel whirring all day long. Eli had taken some of the yarn she had spun and dyed to Andris Souplis, the weaver in the village, who made it into brown-and-white-checked linen cloth. Some of the cloth Mom kept to make into shirts for Pop and Eli. Some of it Eli had taken to the village store to sell. He liked making the bargain with the storekeepers, seeing the people in the village, and hearing Jonas Eidmuller say, "Geese down makes thick, und squirrel tail makes bushy, *so* a hard vinter comes—ain't?" or "Thick shucks on de corn, and leaves from de trees come off from de tops first, *so* lots of schnow und ice dis vinter, think?"

Mom knew he liked taking the yarn to the village and selling the linen at the store, but she said, "The letters you must know and how to do sums, or how can you tell what is right to get for the linen? A smart boy knows how to read, too."

When he reached home, Mom said, "Get right now to work at the flax. My spindle is empty, and only a little iss left in the barn ready for the hackle." So there was no time to do any work on the bench after all, but Mom was pleased when Eli told her that he was to read the Scriptures at the opening of school in the morning.

As he worked, Eli thought, "I will read so well tomorrow that Master Christopher will give me a beautiful picture I can give to Mom." All afternoon Eli slammed the flax brake up and down. He didn't stop except for the time it took to bring Star from the pasture down by the Skippack. Pop kept her in the shed at night, now that the frost had come.

When Eli had a bundle of flax ready for the hackle, he took it into the barn. He wasn't anxious to get back to the flax brake. He stood for a moment watching Star, who stood in the stall chewing her cud. Everything was so still! Except for Star's munching, there wasn't a sound.

"It wonders me now," Eli thought, "did ever a cow jump over the moon? What would a cow look like if she could dance?" Star stood perfectly still chewing her cud. Eli's eyes wandered to the oxgoad that hung beside the bin.

"It wonders me, what would Star do if I should juu-usst *touch* her with that." He lifted the goad down and tiptoed over to Star's stall. He flicked gently at Star's round side with the tip of the goad. She moved suddenly to one side. Eli chuckled. He tried it again. She danced! Then he struck her again, this time on the flank and a bit harder. Star fairly pranced! Eli was filled with delight. He lifted the goad and brought it down smartly over Star's back. She lifted her dainty hoofs clear of the floor, her tail swung up, and she *mooed*. This was fun! Next, Eli laid the switch on still harder, and right where the flesh was most tender. Star plunged and pranced. She bellowed in fright and pain—*but—so—did—Eli!* Pop had come in. Taking Eli by the shirtband and trousers, he lifted him clear of the floor. Then Pop took the oxgoad and laid it on where he thought it would do the most good. "Now," Pop said, "into the house you go and to bed."

Mom looked up in surprise but said nothing as
Eli went up the stairs.

Eli undressed and lay down. He couldn't sleep.
He lay for a long time awake and miserable. It
hurt where Pop had whipped him, but it hurt more
inside when he thought that maybe Pop would send
word to Master Christopher, and he wouldn't be
allowed to read the Scriptures the next day. Finally
he went to sleep.

It was still black dark when he heard Pop go out to hitch up Buck and Berry for market, and not quite light when he was awakened again by a loud knocking, and Mom calling from the bed corner.

"Eli, Eli, come! Somesing makes by the door, and Pop's gone by the German Town." The pounding on the door kept up, and a voice called, "Mrs. Shrawder, Mrs. Shrawder!" So Mom wrapped a bed quilt around her, hurried to light a candle, and went to the door. The baby began to cry, and Sibilla woke up to see what was the matter. Before Eli could get into his trousers and down the ladder, Mom lifted the bar from the door and opened the upper half. There stood Katie Kreider all out of breath, her face white and drawn. When Mom saw who it was, she opened the lower half of the door and Katie came in.

"Margareth's taken bad with her foot again. She stepped on a rusty nail, and the nail we greased and hung it in the chimbly, like our mother used to do; but now she is bad again, the foot as big as a barrel." Mom didn't waste time in talking. She put the candle down. Then she dressed behind the bed curtains, fed the crying baby, and wrapped her

up warmly to be taken along. She went to the painted chest, gathered up her herbs and some pieces of flannel, and put them into a little cloth bag that she carried on her arm.

Katie lived with her sister down the road and back through the forest. Her sister Margareth's husband had bought the land there and begun to clear it but had been killed by a falling tree. Now the two sisters lived alone and found it hard to run a farm in the wilderness without a man to help. Mom had been a friend to them in their trouble as she was to many others and, because she knew something of medicines and herbs, was called upon to help where there was sickness. Often Mom was called out in the middle of the night, but Pop had always been there before to look after the children.

"Na come, Katie," said Mom, "you carry these flannels. Eli," she called over her shoulder, "Sibby you must care for till I come back. Sleep now." Blowing out the candle, Mom took the baby, went out after Katie, and closed the door. Sibilla wailed. Eli lay down beside her on the pallet. He comforted her as best he could with nursery rhymes, and soon they were both asleep.

HE SUN coming through a crack in the logs woke Eli. The morning felt strange. There was no smell of breakfast, no warmth of a fire, no sound of the baby nor of Mom moving about. Then he remembered. Mom had gone with Katie before daylight, and she wasn't back yet. Eli crept down the ladder to look at the tall clock. It was almost time for school! School! And he was to read the Scriptures and perhaps get a present from Master Christopher! But he couldn't go to school and leave Sibilla alone! He couldn't take her to school either. It was too far. He had looked forward to this day for so long. Now he wouldn't get the present for reading well. He stood looking at the clock—it ticked slowly on.

Sibilla woke up. He ran up the ladder and helped her to dress, then put on his own clothes. Sibilla wanted her breakfast, so he tried to hurry. One stocking went on wrong side out. That meant good luck, so he wouldn't change it. He thought he needed all the good luck he could find with a house and little sister to care for. Eli was hungry, too, because Pop had sent him to bed without his supper. He dipped his hands in the basin on the wash bench and patted his face gingerly. How to get breakfast? That was the question. Always before, when it was time for breakfast, good crackling sounds came from the fireplace, where Mom had scrapple or sausage cooking on the trivet, and warmth came up the ladder to the loft. Now, there was just a spark of fire, and the early morning was frosty and cold. Sibilla cried for Mom.

"Don't cry, Sibby, I'll make up the fire, see if I don't." He went to the woodbox and took out chips that he put on the embers a few at a time till there was a little blaze. Then small sticks, and finally "round" wood, round pieces with the bark still on. They made a good steady fire, Eli knew. Sibilla grew so interested she forgot to cry and picked up her little wooden doll from the floor.

"Now," said Eli, "it wonders me what we can make for breakfast." He had no idea how Mom made corn-meal pudding. He did not know how to cook scrapple or sausage.

"Well," said he, "there's milk in the springhouse and bread in the crock. We could have that. Stay here, Sibby, till I get it." Sibby looked as if she might cry again, but Eli shook his finger at her and said, "You know what Master Christopher says, 'Never are we alone.' And anyway, *I'm* here to take care of you." As he said that, he suddenly felt very brave, and Sibilla puckered up her chin and swallowed her tears.

Just as he was about to pick up the pitcher for milk, he heard a lowing from the barn.

"Why, that's Star," he said. "She hasn't been milked! What shall we do?" Mom always did the milking. Eli had only tried it once when he begged Mom to let him.

"Well, now, I *must* try. Mom says she must be milked every morning and night. Sibby, you can come with, but here's your shawl. It's cold. You must be quiet, so Star won't move fast and upset! The pigs we must feed, too, and the geese."

Eli took the milk bucket instead of the pitcher,

and they went out to the log shed. He took down the milking stool. He filled a cup with grain from the feed box for the geese and handed it to Sibby, saying, "Take this to the goose pen and then let them loose."

"Come, Boss!" he said as he had heard Mom do when she wanted Star to move over. Her eyes looked enormous as he fastened the bar across to keep her in the stall. She mooed mournfully as if she knew that Eli was not the one to care for her. "It wonders me," he thought, "if she knows I'm the one that made her dance last night." Sibilla went off to feed the geese.

"Sibby," called Eli, "go once, now, and throw down some hay. She's maybe hungry and will stand *so* if we feed her." Sibilla climbed to the loft and threw down the sweet-smelling hay. Eli set the stool in place and went to work. Star munched the hay but was uneasy at the strange hands milking her. No milk would come! Eli tried and tried. Then he remembered how Mom said, "Gentle, you must be." All of a sudden milk spurted into the bucket. Eli was so excited that he almost forgot to be gentle. The milk rang against the side of the bucket, and soon it was filled. He carried the milk to the springhouse, poured it into a pitcher, then turned Star out to pasture. Wouldn't Mom be glad he could milk! Sibilla clapped her hands and ran for a mug. Eli filled it and then one for himself. The warm milk felt good, and with bread, spread with new apple butter, was all the breakfast they needed.

The big clock struck nine. School time, Eli thought, and he wasn't there to read the Scriptures. He had other things to worry about. The woodbox needed filling, but first he must turn the pigs loose. When they went squealing into the woods, Eli felt as if he and Sibby were alone in the world. Except for the little clearing Pop had made, the forest was all about them. To be sure, it was only a mile or so to the nearest neighbor, but the trees were so high that not even the smoke from the chimney could be seen. Then usually, Mom could be heard singing somewhere about, or Pop could be heard cutting wood, but now there wasn't a sound except the crows cawing and the dry leaves blowing in the wind. Eli believed what Master Christopher had said, "Never are we alone," but he *did* wish Pop or Mom would come home. Even Buck and Berry, the oxen, weren't home. They had drawn the load to market. Pop took things to market for several of the farmers who had no oxen. He took cheeses, rags for the paper mill, flax yarn to the stocking mill, and vegetables. In return the farmers gave fodder for the oxen and the cow.

Eli called Sibby to help fill the woodbox; then he took the broom and swept up the chips that had fallen.

As he stood there in the silence, it came to Eli that there was still some work to do on the bench. He went into the shed and set to work with the piece of pumice stone that Pop had brought from Germany, rubbing the wood to a satin smoothness. He remembered, then, that Pop was going to ask about trading the bench for window glass today in the German Town.

And the more he polished the wood, the sadder he felt. He took the bench in and set it by the fireplace. It was just right, just what Mom wanted,

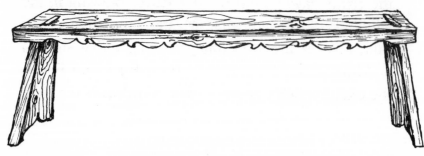

and it really did look like the one they had left in Germany. He sat for a minute, enjoying it but thinking sadly, too, that if he hadn't thrown that ball, Mom would be having it. How could he ever make up for his mischief? He wondered if Pop had found a place to sell or trade the bench. He half wished nobody would buy it; then he could leave it there for Mom. It looked so nice.

At last he decided it must surely be noon, but when he looked at the clock, it was only halfway through the morning, so he went back to work at the flax brake. Sibby was happy with her doll playing in the leaves. Then she brought out her little rocker and played house. The frost had gone with the rising of the sun, and the air was mild and pleasant.

Sibby began to be hungry again. Eli did wish Mom would come to cook dinner. He was hungry, too.

The cupboard seemed to be almost bare, for it was baking day, so they ate more "butter bread." Sibilla took such big bites that her face was smeared with apple butter from ear to ear.

"Look, now," said Eli, "how your face is dirty. See how Mom's soft soap gives a clean face!" He held up the wet washcloth. Sibilla shut her eyes tight and lifted up her face for Eli to wash. The door opened. Sibby waited for the wet cloth to touch her face, but Eli just stood with it in his hand. Sibby opened her eyes. Eli was staring at the door. Sibby turned to look, too. There in the doorway stood *an Indian!*

"Ugh!" he grunted. "Me—White Eagle! Want food—hungry!" He rubbed his stomach round and round. Eli felt as if everything inside *his* stomach were going round and round. Then he saw the scar on White Eagle's cheek. It was the same Indian who had gone by on the road in the summer, and he remembered how Pop had said that the Indians of Pennsylvania were friendly and that a little food and kindness to them meant a great deal. So he answered as Master Christopher had taught him to do.

"Yes, Master White Eagle," and, putting down the wet cloth, went to look in the cupboard again. Sibby clung to Eli and tried to hide behind him, but she didn't cry. There was only a small piece of shoofly pie, that Mom had made of molasses and spices, and some cold corn-meal mush, but White Eagle seemed to think it a feast. He ate it almost

149

before Eli had time to put it before him. Then he sighed and drank in great gulps the milk Eli brought him. Sibby had crept behind the bed curtains and just peeked out, but Eli stood beside the table where White Eagle was. He looked at the shell earrings, at the strings of ermine hide hanging at each side of White Eagle's head, at the colored beads on his naked chest, and the armlets. There was an eagle feather standing out at the back of his head, and he had a great dignity about him. He had a sober yet friendly look, and when he saw Eli was without fear, he began to talk. He spread out his arms in a slow motion and said, "Land—White Eagle's one time; now white man's. White Man— my friend."

Then in his slow speech he told about his father, one of the Lenni Lenape Tribe who had made the treaty with William Penn at Shackamaxon. He told how they had always kept the treaty. He made pictures for Eli to show how he made his mark. It was a white eagle in flight. Finally he got up and said, "Now, me go. Go see White Chief for Council. Go city of Onas, our brother, Penn."

He got up on his pony and rode away. While Eli watched him disappear into the woods, he saw

Mom coming with the baby. He ran to meet her and helped her carry the things she had taken to Katie Kreider's.

While Mom was putting away her things, Eli was telling her how they got breakfast, how Sibby had fed the geese, and how he had milked the cow so he and Sibby had fresh milk for breakfast; about the visit of White Eagle and how hungry he and Sibby had been.

"Ach," said Mom, "what a big day it makes! This early morning I meant to come home, but so sick was Margareth I must stay by till she was better. Such a big boy you are so Mom could trust you. Yah well, the Good Book says no one knows what a day may bring forth." She smoothed Eli's hair.

There were all the evening chores to be done— Star to be brought in and milked, the geese to be tended, and the pigs brought in. Eli hurried out to the barn.

Just as Mom had supper nearly ready, they heard the wagon creaking through the wood and the slow tread of Buck and Berry.

"Just in time now," said Mom as she lighted the candles. Eli helped Pop put the oxen up for the night, and just as Mom called them for supper, someone else came riding through the wood clop! clop! on the dry earth. It was Master Christopher on his black horse, Firefly.

FTER SUPPER, Master Christopher said, "This is a fine solid bench I've been sitting on. It is well carved, too. Would that be the bench you made, Eli? If it is, I'm sure that would sell in the German Town."

"Ach yes," said Pop. "I saw Master Casper Weimar today who buys glass in South Jersey. He said if the bench is well made, it will pay for the glass. Next time I go to the German Town I take it and get the glass."

Eli couldn't say a word. His last hope was gone.

Mom glanced at him. "Yes, a good bench it is. Eli has worked hard. He should be proud that he can make such a good one to trade. For me, he can make another one."

"Yes, Eli should be thankful, too, that so soon the bench is finished," Master Christopher said. "We will be needing that window. And Eli has been a good boy today, too, I can see. I know now why he didn't come to school when he was to read the Scriptures.

"Dear child," he turned to Eli, "maybe you would like to come with me to the German Town to school tomorrow? I have some errands to do as well. Some paper to buy at the paper mill and business at the printer's. Would you like to come?"

Would he! Eli could hardly believe his ears! Really *see* all the shops? Really stop in the market and perhaps go to the paper mill? It seemed too good to be true! Every time Master Christopher had gone to the German Town, Eli had wished he might go along.

Pop nodded, and Mom said, "Ach! Yah, you could go," as if she knew the trip would help him to forget the bench. Then Mom helped him tie his things in a bundle. He would have to stay the three days and could sleep at Cousin Jacob's fine house. It was hard for Eli to go to bed in the loft that night. Master Christopher slept on the settle before the fire.

They were up before daylight, and Mom had breakfast for them. She had cooked more cornmeal mush before going to bed, and it was ready to fry in the spider. Eli said he wasn't hungry, but Mom said, "It makes long till dinnertime, Eli. Eat once, now."

The morning was fine when they set out, but chilly in the starlight before the dawn. Shadows were deep in the woods. As they rode through the trees, Eli held tight to the master, who said, "The Book says, 'Thy word shall be a light unto my Path.' " Eli loved the smell of dry leaves, of smoke as they passed a cabin, and of the wild grapes. He liked the sound of the horse's hoofs on the frosty road, that widened as they came to the village.

They rode through the wide marsh and on up the hill over the Bethlehem Road into the German Town. It was just about time for school when they drew up in front of the log meetinghouse where school was kept. The school looked different from the Skippack School. The benches had a back rail and faced the front of the room. Instead of a desk on the platform, Master Christopher had a table.

When noontime came, the master said to Eli, "Go now, dear child, to thy Cousin Hannah's and

let her know you are here. Tell her you may be a
little late getting home this afternoon, and do not
linger on the way. You will have just time! You
go down past the Market Square till you come to
Grumblethorpe. Cousin Hannah's is just beyond."

Eli wanted to stop to see everything all along
the German Town Road. Especially in the Market
Square and at the Green Tree Inn, where the stable-
boys were busy attending to travelers and a carriage

that had arrived from Philadelphia. But he had been told to be quick. So he hurried on.

Cousin Hannah made him very welcome and must hear from him all about the log house and how Barbara was growing. She had heard all the news from Pop, but she liked to hear Eli tell it.

"And me," he said, "I know my letters and can read!"

After dinner with Cousin Hannah and Cousin Jacob, Eli went back to school. The afternoon was much the same as the morning session—reading, sums, and a short time at singing.

When school was over, Master Christopher said with a twinkle in his eye, "Eli, I must go to the mill for some paper to take back to the Skippack School. Would you want to go enough to help me sweep the schoolroom?"

Eli just grinned at the master and set to work. *Now* he knew why he'd been told to say he'd be late getting home! He made the dust fly so thick that Master Christopher began to cough.

"Not so fast, not so fast!" he said. "Do it *so!*" and he showed Eli how to draw the broom over the rough floor so the dust wouldn't fly.

Then off they went together.

The paper mill was so interesting! Eli watched the rags of old clothing go in at one end of the mill, where they were cut in pieces. Then they went through the big vats that took out all the color, and through other great vats that dissolved the rags into a thick pulp. The pulp went through the huge vats, presses, and rollers, then came out as beautiful creamy-white paper with the Rittenhouse water-mark upon it.

Master Rittenhouse gave Eli two or three sheets of the paper to take home. Eli thanked him— never before had he had any paper of his own. It would be fun to write on his own paper. "Perhaps," he thought, "if I make a journal and write about all the things I've seen in the German Town, it will please Master Christopher."

By the time they left the paper mill, the sun was low, and it was beginning to be very cool. Master Christopher put Eli before him on the horse to keep him warm. They rode up the Rittenhouse Lane and over to the German Town Road, down past the Market Square where the shops were closing, past the Friends' Meetinghouse, past the Green Tree Tavern, and to Cousin Hannah's. Candles were lighted, and Cousin Jacob was home.

They invited Master Christopher to have supper with them, and afterwards sat talking before the fire until Eli fell asleep. Cousin Jacob picked him up gently and carried him to bed.

"School again on Friday," Eli wrote in his journal the next day. He had folded the paper into a little book and had already written about all that he had seen on Thursday.

Eli waited for Master Christopher again after school, for he had told Cousin Hannah he would take Eli with him to Christopher Sauer's printing office.

The printing office was below the school and the Market Square, and there were all kinds of things to be seen on the way. There was the tannery, the Bringhurst coach works, the stocking mill, and lots of shops and fine houses. But the Sauer Printing Shop that stood back of the house on the German Town Road was the most interesting of all.

Master Christopher Sauer greeted Master Christopher Dock warmly. They were great friends.

"And this is my little friend, Eli Shrawder," said the schoolmaster. "He would like to see how a book is made. We have seen how the paper is made at Rittenhouse's mill."

"To be sure, to be sure," said Master Sauer. He led the way to the little office. The desk was piled with papers, with almanacs, with bills stuck on sharp pointed files, and with several blocks on which were pictures cut into the wood.

Master Sauer saw Eli looking again and again at the wooden blocks on the desk. He picked one up and showed Eli how the picture was cut into the wood.

"You see," he said, "the man in the picture is using his left hand instead of his right hand, because when the picture is printed, it will be turned over like this." He showed Eli the print made from the block and explained how the ink was spread on the surface. Eli listened to every word and hated to leave the fascinating blocks. To cut designs in wood and see them printed would be even more exciting than carving a bench or a fan. But there was a smell of ink in the air and the sound of the press from the back room, and he wanted to see what was going on there. First Master Sauer showed them the finished books. Some were hymn books printed for the Mennonites, some were books of Psalms, and one was a child's book. It was very small, just right for a child to hold, and it had two pictures in it. It had a very long title, *The Story of Little Gabriel, or the Sin of Lying. Being a Moral Tale for the Instruction of the Young.* Eli wished he could have it, but books cost a great deal of money. Then he had another idea! It made him so excited that his scalp prickled. He didn't mention it, however, for perhaps it wouldn't work.

Master Sauer led them back to the pressroom. A man stood at a high bench sorting type and setting it in what he said was a "type stick." A boy apprentice, who was learning the trade of printing, was mixing ink. He said it was made of nutgall to make it black, gum arabic to make it hold together, and vinegar to thin it so it would spread. Everywhere around the walls were pieces of paper tacked up, notices of news in the town, information to be put in the almanac, the signs of the zodiac, and bits of decorations to put around borders and at the heads of the columns. Eli had never seen such a fascinating place. He longed to work the lever of the press and see the printed matter come out clean and bright.

Master Sauer must have seen how much he was interested, for he said, "Would you like to run this paper through the press?"

162

Even though he was so excited, he remembered to answer as he had been taught. "Yes, Master Sauer, more than anything I would like it!" He eagerly reached for the lever.

"Vait! Vait!" said Master Sauer. "You must put the paper in *so,* with the corner close against the mark. *Now—pull hard!"* Eli did pull hard, but Master Sauer had to help him. Then Eli helped lift the paper carefully off the press. It turned out to be one sheet of the almanac. Each sheet was printed on both sides and folded into four so that it made eight pages. It had a picture on it, too, for the title page, and the signs of the zodiac to tell when it was time to make sauerkraut, when was the best time to cure hams, the best time to dig potatoes, and how to cure a cow of mooing for her calf.

"Now such a good printer's boy you have been, you shall have a copy of this almanac to take home to your father to read," Master Sauer said. Then he took Eli's sheet and put with it the one to complete the almanac and gave it to Eli.

This time Eli was so happy that he almost forgot to say "Thank you," but he caught Master Christopher's eye and remembered in time.

"Thank you, Master Sauer," he said. "I shall keep it always."

The next day was Saturday, but school was kept as usual. Eli lingered on the way, because there was so much to see in the Market Square. Farmers were weighing wagonloads of wood and of hay in the weighhouse. People were buying food in the food stalls; servants were carrying loaded baskets after their mistresses. Ladies in white kerchiefs and caps, gentlemen in knee breeches and buckled shoes greeted each other and passed, and the tavern yard was crowded with vehicles.

When noontime came, the Market Square was more crowded than ever. When Eli got here, he saw the reason. In the Square, right out in the open, was a large round oaken table. Seated at the table and eating heartily were eight Indians! Waiting upon them, with great platters of food, were the women of the village. Even the women seemed to be enjoying it, and there among the Indians was White Eagle, Eli's friend! Eli didn't go near; there were too many strangers. But he watched for a while, then went on his way to Cousin Hannah's. When he told her about the Indians feasting in the Market Square, she said,

"Ach yes! Whenever those Indians go through the German Town on their way to the Council in Philadelphia, they must have a feast here in the Square. But so! It keeps them good friends, and never have they broken the Penn Treaty. Cousin Jacob says the settlers far west are having trouble with Indians. That is why they have the Council. We can be glad that no child need fear the Indians here!"

After dinner, Cousin Hannah sent him back to school, and the last afternoon session began.

My Son Keep God before and thine eyes in thy heart

FTER SCHOOL, Master Christopher took Eli to his lodging place to get his things. There they mounted Firefly and went to Cousin Hannah's to bid her good-by and get Eli's bundle.

Cousin Hannah sent messages to Pop and Mom and some "sweets for the kinder," Sibilla and Barbara Ann. Eli climbed up on Firefly behind Master Christopher, and they started for home. It was still afternoon and perfect October weather.

They went up past the printing shop, through the Market Square again, and past the school. They passed the little stone building where the Lutheran School was kept and on out the German Town Road.

169

Down the big hill they went into the maple and oak forests blazing with color. Master Christopher began to sing, and Eli joined him. They kept time to the horse's hoofbeats, and he in turn kept time to the music, so they frisked along at a lively canter.

In about an hour, they came to the wide marsh again and to the Skippack Road, where the Farmer's Mill stood. Before long, the sun went down behind the hills. For a while, the sky was a golden yellow, and the trees looked darker and darker till they were almost black. By the time they came to the Inden Hoffen Tavern the yellow had faded from the sky and the light was gone. When they reached the village, Eli was so tired that he fell asleep and would have fallen from the horse, but Master Christopher caught him in time and set him before him so he shouldn't fall again. It was candlelight when they reached the cabin, where Mom was standing in the door to meet them. She had heard the hoofbeats coming through the wood. Master Christopher helped Eli off the horse, then went on home.

Mom had a great kettle of pepper pot for supper, and Pop came in from the barn just as she was dishing it into the pewter bowls. The hot soup took the sleepiness away, and Eli began to tell about all the things he had seen in the German Town. He told about the Indians feasting in the Market Square, about the paper mill, and about the printing shop at Master Sauer's. That made him remember the almanac, and the sweets for Sibilla and for Barbara Ann, but he didn't tell them about the idea he had.

He had put the folded paper journal in his inside coat pocket, so he said nothing about it but took it up to bed with him and laid it carefully on the candle shelf that jutted out from the wall. He wished he could get right at what he had in mind, but the next day was Sunday, and no unnecessary work could be done.

The animals must be cared for, of course, and simple food prepared, but most of the day was spent at the long preaching service in the meeting-house by the school. Then after a dinner of cold food, Pop read the Scriptures aloud and they sang hymns. But all the while, Eli was thinking of his idea and how he would carry it out. At last it was time for the evening hymn, and the long day was over.

Very early Monday morning, while Eli was gathering the wood, he found a square piece that was just what he wanted. He hid it in the loft so Mom wouldn't burn it by mistake. He didn't want to tell her what it was for. He wanted to see first whether he could work out his plan.

During school, Master Christopher said to him, "Eli, would you like to tell the boys and girls about all the things you saw in the German Town?"

But Eli said, "I am not quite ready yet, sir."

"Very well, then," said Master Christopher; "perhaps Wednesday afternoon we shall hear it. Will you be ready then?" The teacher smiled. He knew that Eli must have some special reason for waiting to tell his story. He said, "You know if you do well these two days, you are to read the Scriptures that day, too, my boy."

"Yes, Master Christopher," said Eli. "And please could I have some of that ink you keep in the drawer?"

"Of course," said the teacher. "You must be working at home!"

Eli laughed but said only, "Thank you," and tucked the paper of dry ink into his pocket. After school he hurried home to start work.

When he got home, Mom wondered what he was up to. He raced through the house, dropping his hat and book as he went up the ladder to the loft, then down and out to the shed, where he kept very busy till Mom called him to help her.

Tuesday Eli could hardly wait for school to be over so that he could get back to work on his surprise. He didn't wait for Amos or for Claus, but ran all the way home alone. He couldn't waste time playing until he had finished his surprise for Master Christopher. It was the most interesting thing he had done since the bench was finished.

As soon as he opened the door, he threw down his hat and horn book and went to the loft to find the precious journal and the special thing he was working on. Mom stopped her spinning and looked up as he came down the ladder.

"Shh!" she said with her finger to her lips. "What makes such a hurry? Barbara Ann has just gone to sleep. And Sibby, too, sleeps on the bed."

"Mom," Eli whispered as he put the block of wood and the pages of the journal down on the table, "can I have an egg and some vinegar?"

"*Egg?*" said Mom. "What for? It is not the time for breakfast. And vinegar? What is it you are doing?"

"I need it for something—something *nice. Please* can I have it?"

Mom smiled. She got up from her wheel and opened the cupboard. She took one of the goose eggs from a bowl and gave it to Eli and poured some vinegar from the jug into a cup. He picked up two little doll-sized bowls from Sibby's play cupboard and broke the egg into them, the yolk in one bowl, the white in the other. Then he went to the dye kettle out in the open shed that Pop had built and dipped up some of the blue dye in a saucer. He went to the hearth and took a feather from the turkey-wing brush.

Mom watched while he spread out all the things on the table beside the little book he had made, but she kept quiet. She thought to herself how much Eli was like her brother, how much he liked to make things. Eli went straight to work. With his pocket knife, he scraped the feather down to a

small brush. He mixed some of the vinegar with the powdered ink. The yolk of the egg was bright yellow. He mixed some of the blue dye with the egg yolk in another little dish to make green. It was just right! Then using the white of egg with the dye, he made a lovely, glossy blue. Eli worked for a long time. Once he stopped to run out to the shed and came in with Pop's mallet.

Mom was so interested that she forgot to spin. When he had done the best he could, he held what he had been making for Mom to see. "Ach!" she said, "so beautiful it iss!" She brought a needle threaded with yarn and showed Eli how to fasten the pages of the book together at the back.

When Wednesday came, Eli took pains to make his hair smooth and neat and put on the clean shirt Mom had ironed for him. He took the almanac from the wall and carried the little journal safely tucked between its leaves. He was in his place at school before Amos or Tobias had come in sight and had slid the almanac with the hidden journal into his desk.

The Scripture reading of the First Psalm went very well. Even the word "meditate" was not too much for Eli, but all day long he could hardly wait to show Master Christopher the journal and the secret he had made, and to read to the children.

Finally the arithmetic exercises were all finished, recess and dinnertime came and passed, and the girls had their reading lesson. Then the singing lesson came. Finally it was over. Master Christopher stood with his hands behind him and called on Eli to rise.

"So you are ready now, my boy, to tell us about the German Town? Let the children hear about it."

Eli took the little book from his desk. Everyone turned to look at him as he rose, and he suddenly felt very shy. Then he looked down at the little book. Should he show it to the teacher first or read it first? The boys and girls watched him expectantly, so he began to read all he had written.

The children listened closely. They didn't make a sound until Eli finished reading. Master Christopher, too, seemed to listen as if he had never seen all the things that Eli told about.

Eli closed the little book, smoothed the cover, and handed it to the teacher.

"This I made for you, sir," he said. "It is not so fine as Master Sauer makes, but it was the best I could do. I hope you will like it."

Master Christopher took the book and looked at it in surprise. The cover had on it a picture printed in ink and decorated in color. It was a simple design of a flower and leaves, but it looked very pretty.

"Ach!" said the master, "for *me?* Why, dear child, you have made a *wood block* and printed it on the cover! That is very well done. Even I have never made a wood block! You have colored it, too! How did you ever get the colors?"

All the children turned eagerly toward the master to see what Eli had done. The master held the book up so all could see. Then he asked Eli to tell just how he had done it.

Eli told how he had marked the outline of the picture first with a piece of charred stick on the block of wood, then carved out the design with his knife and Pop's small chisel; how he had mixed the ink with vinegar and printed the picture by pressing the block down on the paper and tapping it with

Pop's mallet. He told about mixing the color with egg and dye, and then how Mom had given him needle and thread and shown him how to sew the leaves together at the back. Everyone listened.

When he had finished, Master Christopher said, "I shall keep this as a real treasure, my boy. Now," he said, reaching into the drawer of his desk, "I think you have really earned a present from me, and you shall have it." He brought out a beautiful painting with birds and flowers for decoration, a line of Scripture, and the alphabet in both capitals and small letters.

A ripple of "Ahs!" went around the room as it was held up for the children to see.

Eli took it. "Oh, thank you, Master Christopher," he said. He thought it was the most beautiful one the master had made. He held the paper carefully till the benediction was said, then tucked it smoothly under his jacket and ran home as fast as he could go to show it to Mom. As he ran, he imagined how nice it would look over the fireplace. He could make a carved frame for it.

Mom heard him running through the dry leaves and opened the door with Barbara on her arm and Sibilla peeping from behind her apron.

Eli held behind him the present from Master Christopher. He couldn't keep from chuckling, so Mom knew that he had a surprise for her.

"It wonders me now," she said, "what iss it that you have?" Eli couldn't wait any longer. He held out the picture and spread it on the table where the light shone on it. Together, Mom and Eli read it through and looked at all the decorations and beautiful colors.

"Ach, that iss fine," said Mom. "A good boy you have been to learn your letters and please Master Christopher."

"And, Mom," Eli burst out, "soon I will carve a frame for it. Then it can hang over the fireplace."

Mom nodded. "Nice that will be, but now we put it in a safe place." She went to get the great Family Bible. She smoothed the present carefully, to lay between the leaves until Eli could make the frame. Just where the Bible happened to open was this verse; so Mom read it aloud: "THY WORD IS A LAMP UNTO MY FEET, AND A LIGHT UNTO MY PATH."

Think It Over

1. In *Roads to Follow* you have been learning about some people who came to America for the same reason the Shrawders did. Who were these people? What was their reason for coming?
2. What did the people of Penn's Woods do for the Shrawders to show their friendliness? What are some ways in which people today show their friendliness to newcomers in a town or neighborhood?
3. Old sayings like "Thirteen is an unlucky number" and "It is bad luck to break a mirror" are based on beliefs that cannot be proved. In this story, what was the old German belief about the time that fence posts and buildings should be set in the ground? Make a list of the old sayings or beliefs that you know.
4. What are some of the differences between your school and Skippack School?
5. What was Eli's worst problem at school?
6. In what way did Master Christopher reward the children for learning their letters?

7. What happened to make Eli think he would never get a flower painting? Why did Master Christopher send a note to Eli's parents?

8. Why was Eli making a bench for his mother? How do you know he enjoyed carving the bench?

9. Why did Pop say that Eli's bench had to be sold? Do you think he was being fair? Why?

10. Name five or more interesting things that Eli saw or did on his visit to the German Town with Master Christopher.

11. What did Eli see at the paper mill? What was he given there that he had never had before?

12. What did the signs of the zodiac tell?

13. What surprise did Eli plan for his teacher? What does this tell you about his feeling for Master Christopher?

14. What is a wood block? How did Eli make one?

15. How did Master Christopher show that he appreciated Eli's work?

Looking Back

The Pilgrims came to America in 1620. By the time the Shrawders arrived, about 1750, many things had changed. But many things remained almost the same. What are some of the changes? What had remained almost the same? In what ways was Eli's life somewhat like your own?

New Words for Old

Because this story takes place many years ago, some of the words in it are not used much today. Copy the sentences that follow, but change the underlined word in each one to a word that we would probably use today.

1. The women wore plain dresses and white kerchiefs and caps.
2. The schoolmaster sent a note home complaining of Eli's mischief and lack of attention.
3. Master Christopher put on his spectacles.
4. Master Christopher slept on the settle before the fire.
5. She had cooked more corn-meal mush, and it was ready to fry in the spider.
6. The afternoon was very much the same as the morning session—reading, sums, and a short time at singing.

7. The animals must be cared for, of course, and simple food prepared, but most of the day was spent at the long preaching service in the meetinghouse by the school.

Make a Match

The twelve words from *Skippack School* listed below may have seemed strange to you. Each of the phrases that follow the words explains one of them. Copy each word. Then write after it the phrase that explains it.

1. Eckball
2. shoofly pie
3. springhouse
4. trundle bed
5. scrapple
6. quill pen

7. spelling bee
8. flax
9. dowry
10. oxgoad
11. pepper pot
12. watermark

a. something to eat made of corn meal and pork scraps
b. a game of ball
c. a contest to see which person can spell better than all the others

d. a stick to drive oxen
e. something that is moved on rollers and fits under another bed
f. a shed or house in which food is kept, built near a spring
g. something to eat made of molasses, spices, and mush
h. something used in writing
i. a plant from which linen thread is made
j. a kind of stew
k. the money or other valuable things a woman brings to the man she marries
l. a nearly invisible design in certain kinds of paper

More Books to Read

BULLA, CLYDE ROBERT. *Down the Mississippi.* New York: Thomas Y. Crowell Company, 1954.

Erik tries to like farming, but all the time he dreams about becoming a riverman and going down the Mississippi. When his cousin Gunder stops by unexpectedly, Erik has his chance. The trip they take is dangerous at times, and Erik must decide if this is really the life for him.

COLVER, ANNE. *Bread-and-Butter Indian.*
New York: Holt, Rinehart and Winston, 1964.

This is the true story of a little pioneer girl and her secret Indian friend. The excitement mounts when an uprising occurs and Barbara is kidnaped.

FIELD, ELSIE KIMMELL. *Prairie Winter.*
New York: Lothrop, Lee & Shepard Co., Inc., 1959.

After railroads had been built to the West, people came to settle there and begin farming the land. *Prairie Winter* is the story of a family of settlers and their first winter on the Dakota plains.

WILDER, LAURA INGALLS. *Little House in the Big Woods.*
New York: Harper & Row, Publishers, Inc., 1932, 1953.

This is a warm family story about a real little girl. Laura Ingalls Wilder tells of her life as a pioneer girl and about both the everyday and the unusual things that happened to her.

Lee Kingman was an only child. To keep from feeling lonesome, she read a great deal, particularly stories about big families. When she was in junior high school, she was "turning out stories and poems like a barrel organ" and knew that she wanted to be a writer. She has written a great many books for children. These include *The Saturday Gang, Peter's Long Walk,* and *Peter's Pony.*

Miss Kingman lives with her husband and two children on Cape Ann, Massachusetts, in a house that they helped build. She is very much interested in art and enjoys making pottery, raising sheep, and growing trees.

PHILIPPE'S HILL

LEE KINGMAN
PICTURES BY
HILDEGARD WOODWARD

In the Laurentian Mountains in Canada
was a special little hill. Philippe
thought of it as his hill. He would
climb to its top and dream about the
day when he would have skis and could
fly down its slope and out over the
countryside.

If you've ever made something yourself,
or tried to solve a problem when
no one else could help, you'll enjoy
reading about Philippe and his problem.
After you have read the book, try to
decide what you would have done if you
had been Philippe.

Philippe's Hill

by LEE KINGMAN

Illustrated by HILDEGARD WOODWARD

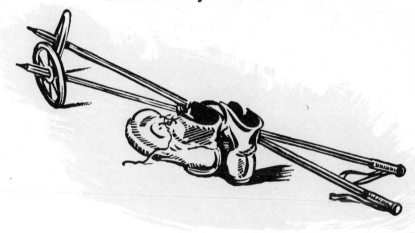

DOUBLEDAY & COMPANY, INC.
Garden City, New York

FOR ALL THE COUSINS

Mary Ann, Laura, Eleanor,
Carol, Diana, Nancy, David,
Erik, Eric, Isabel, Deanie,
John, Selma, Susi, and
Christine

In summertime the great hill behind Philippe's house rolled up toward the sky and wore a green hat of trees. In wintertime the sky leaned down toward the hill and breathed snow on it until it made a brilliant crown above Philippe's house.

Philippe was very fond of his hill. He often climbed to the top and sat there dreaming that it was his world, where only things that he liked would happen.

Philippe Tourneau was nine years old. His hair and eyes were as brown as a glossy chestnut, and he was just the right size for his age.

His house below the hill sat beside a country road in Canada. In summertime only a few friends and neighbors trotted along it with their horses and wagons, or rode by in their bangy old cars.

But in wintertime, when the plows packed shining drift walls along it, the road was merry with bright new cars bringing skiers into the Laurentian Mountains.

In summer Philippe didn't have much time to watch the quiet, dusty road. Nor did he have time very often to sit on his hill and dream. Instead, he spent long, hot hours on the lower slope cutting hay as he helped his father and his older brother, Anton. They would pitch the hay into Anton's old truck and tuck it into the barn so that Michele, the cow, would have plenty to eat during the long, snowy months.

But sometimes at the end of the day Philippe would climb up to the top of his hill. He often wished for things while he was there. For a long time he had wished for three things. He wanted time to play, for his father usually kept him much too busy at jobs on the farm. He wanted someone to play with. And he wanted a beautiful pair of skis like those his brother Anton once had.

At the end of the summer, when school began, Philippe forgot the first two wishes a little. But from the moment the first soft, fuzzy snowflake drifted teasingly down in November until the whole hill was a shining sheet of snow, the third wish for the skis kept up with a busy little ache inside him.

If only Anton's leg that he hurt in a ski accident last winter would stop paining him, and if

only Papa didn't have to count each penny twice,
maybe Mama would let him have skis and Papa
would buy them.

As soon as Philippe jumped off the school bus
and ran into the house, he would take his mug of
chocolate to the front window and watch the cars
go by. Sometimes his father sat and watched, too,
for with snow on the ground there weren't so many
things to do on a farm.

196

Just around two curves in the road was a big hotel for skiers. Often the inn would send a sleigh to meet the train, and Philippe could see the tangle of skis and people in their gay clothes as the horses trotted merrily by, sleigh bells singing out crisply. Philippe wished with all his nine-year-old longing that he were riding along the road with a pair of skis to have an adventure.

He talked earnestly about skis at Christmastime. Surely Mama understood that Philippe would ski carefully and not get hurt, like Anton. Surely Papa knew that Philippe didn't want anything—not one thing—but skis. He almost couldn't believe it when he got a new jacket and new mittens and a new checker set instead. Right then and there Philippe decided wishing wasn't practical enough. He'd have to *do* something about skis.

On a bright, brisk Saturday morning right after Christmas he looked out of his bedroom window at the hill, and it seemed as if the sun were making a special gleaming slide down it just for him.

"Let's ski!" he said to his sister Mimi; she was only seven, but she liked to have adventures, too.

Mimi said, "What can we ski with? Let's just go sliding in dishpans the way we did last year."

"Not any more," Philippe told her firmly. "That's for babies. We'll make some skis." He stamped out of the kitchen into the shed. He could remember just how Anton's tall, swift skis looked when they used to stand in the corner, before he fell in a race and the skis were broken. Anton had been a wonderful skier!

Philippe looked around the shed. He liked to make things. "There's that old barrel in the corner. I've read about using barrel staves for skis. Let's try it."

He took his hammer and bang! knock! bang! The slightly curved staves circled onto the floor with a clattering crash! Philippe tried standing on them, and they did make him feel like a rocking horse. But out in the snow surely they would behave like skis.

"Oh, Philippe!" Mimi laughed, kicking at the funny skis. "How can we keep them on our feet?"

Philippe thought. He couldn't give up now. While he was thinking, he wandered back into the house, into the front parlor. Then he saw just what he needed! His mother's tiebacks for the curtains. They were beautiful felt butterflies on heavy bands of elastic.

"Don't tell Mama, Mimi, but we can borrow these and put them back later." Philippe slipped two pairs off the curtains and rushed back to the shed. He nailed them neatly onto the middle of the barrel staves.

"There!" he said. "I'll bet no one in the world but us has such beautiful ski harnesses!"

He remembered the strong leather and shining steel coils on Anton's big skis, and he felt that butterflies did look a little foolish. "But nothing is foolish as long as it does what it's supposed to do!" he reminded himself. Then he and Mimi plunged into their warmest clothes and out they dashed.

The thick snow was so soft that their feet flung fluffs of it flying up like ocean surf, and in a few minutes, in spite of the crisp Canadian air, their faces felt a delicious moist warmth.

On each side of the hill, marching toward the top, were pine trees. But when Anton had been learning to ski, he had persuaded Papa to chop down the trees in the middle for their winter's wood. So there was an open space three times as wide as the road all the way up the hill.

They trudged halfway up before Philippe turned around. "Let's try it from here!" He helped Mimi onto her skis and gave her a push.

"Ooooooops!" she shrieked, expecting to whiz down the hill with the grace of a grasshopper.

But instead she slid into the soft snow until it clung about her so tightly that her skis stuck in it.

"Oh dear," said Philippe. "You just aren't big enough to go very far. I'll make a path for you."

200

He pushed himself off with the broom he had brought for a ski pole, and whoooooops! He was heavy enough to slide and keep on going!

Swoosh! Swoosh! The snow swished away from his stubby-toed skis, and down the hill he flew, faster and faster!

All of a sudden there he was at the bottom! He was so surprised to be there that he sat down and the snow splashed all around him.

"Come on!" he called to Mimi. The little girl tried to slide in his tracks, but she fell so many times that the hill began to look like a field plowed up for planting.

All morning they slipped and slid and climbed up and skied down again. Philippe's face glowed with happiness as well as exercise. At last he was skiing! At last he knew how it felt to fly down his hill.

Mama rang a bell to call them in for lunch. Philippe had been expecting all morning that she would call them in and tell them not to ski because they might get hurt. But either she had been too busy to notice what they were doing, or else she had decided no one could ski well enough on barrel staves for it to be dangerous.

Philippe and Mimi flew down the hill just as Anton's old truck coughed and sneezed its way into the yard. Anton slid out of the truck.

"Look at us skiing!" Mimi called to Anton.

"I see," said Anton. "You are like birds of flight—so free, so graceful——" he began. But Mimi tumbled, and her skis waved in the air as she slid on her back to a stop. Anton changed his mind. "You are a bird that is better at nesting than at flight," he said as he picked her out of the round wallow she was making. "Didn't anyone tell you that falling down when you're skiing isn't very wise? Good skiers don't do it."

Sometimes Philippe thought Anton's leg hadn't been hurt so much as his pride was in losing the race.

"Look out!" shrieked Philippe as he sped toward them. "There's no way to stop these skis!"

Anton caught him. "Skis?" he asked. Then he saw the barrel staves and his mother's curtain tie-backs, and burst into laughing roars. "What skis! Butterfly-banded, too!"

But when he saw the hurt in Philippe's brown eyes, he shook his brother lovingly. "You did a very clever piece of work, Philippe. But what is Mama going to say about her beautiful butterflies?"

The felt was soggy, and the butterflies' wings drooped sadly.

"They look as if they'd never fly again," said Mimi.

When Mama saw them from the kitchen door, she cried, "Oh, my lovely butterflies! They'll never look right in the parlor again. What were you thinking of, Philippe?"

"I was thinking of skiing," Philippe said. "And the butterflies helped us down the hill so fast!"

Mama wanted to scold him, but Philippe was so earnest that she couldn't. Ever since Anton's accident, when his hospital bills took all their savings right out of the bank, she grew cross whenever she saw skis. And Philippe had done nothing but talk about them since the first snow fell. She sighed. Sometimes it was terribly hard to be a mother and tell Philippe not to do something when he just seemed to wiggle all over with wanting.

"I do wish you'd be careful," Mama said. "Skiing is so dangerous."

"Don't worry." Anton told her. "Philippe and Mimi are right here in the back yard, and those skis are about as dangerous as a rocking chair."

"Oh, Anton!" Philippe's excitement at his skiing fell faster than a snowflake. Somehow he had never thought of his hill as being just back yard!

And of course Anton—who had been able to turn and swing and twist with his skis until he seemed more like a swiftly darting bird than a boy wearing two long planks of wood—couldn't imagine that Philippe on his barrel staves felt just as much a brave skier as he ever had.

Mama sighed again. "There has never been anyone else in this family as determined as Philippe—for which I am thankful. He has talked nothing but skis all winter, and now he has actually gone skiing."

"You might as well get him a good pair," Anton said, "and let him learn how to do it right from the beginning."

"Oh, Anton!" Philippe's eyes were exclamations of eagerness, and forgetting everything about Anton except that he had been a wonderful skier, he burst out, "Will you teach me how to ski?"

"How can I!" Anton said bitterly. "I can show you charts and explain with a lot of words. But the best way to learn is to watch someone and then do it yourself until you get the feel of it and the whole motion just flows from your head right through your toes to the tips of your skis. And I can't show you any more."

"I'm sorry, Anton," Philippe said. "I forgot."

"That's all right," Anton told him as he started toward the house. "Why don't you ask Papa for the skis anyway?"

"That's all I've been doing," Philippe said. "But maybe one more time won't hurt."

Papa was sitting at the kitchen table, scowling at a farm magazine that had pictures of strong tractors and big plows and harrows. Philippe knew that when Papa was scowling it was not a good time to ask for anything. He took off his jacket and decided to wait until after Papa had eaten.

But Anton didn't notice that Papa's storm warnings were flying. "Papa," he said, "Philippe ought to have a pair of skis."

"Me, too!" shouted Mimi, who didn't see why she shouldn't be treated the same as Philippe.

Papa closed the magazine so he couldn't see the tractors and said sadly, "You forget that skis, now they are the fashion, cost lots of money. Before, when we used skis to travel, they were cheap. Now it is a sport, the expense is great." He sighed. "And now we have no money for anything extra. Not for skis—not for tractors—not even for trucks." He frowned at Anton, whose poor old truck always needed new parts and drank too much gasoline, Papa claimed.

"No, I'm sorry. No skis this year. Perhaps next year if I sell the hill to the lumber company that asked about the pine trees——"

"The hill! My hill!" Philippe cried. "What good would skis be without my hill?"

"Whoever buys the hill wouldn't move it, Philippe!" Anton told him. "Besides, if the lumber company took the trees off, there wouldn't be anything for you to bump into."

"But it wouldn't be my hill any more." Philippe couldn't tell them that the hill to him was his world, and so far it was happier when he was the only one in it.

"We'll miss the trees," said Mama. "Gaston, you ought to plant more trees—not cut those down."

"No one is ever pleased, no matter what I do," Papa said in a discouraged voice. "Anton wanted trees cut down. Mama wants trees planted. Philippe doesn't want the hill sold, but he does want skis! That's what is at the bottom of all our troubles—skis! And I'm tired of hearing about them. From now on don't anyone mention skis to me again!"

Papa banged his hand on the table and scowled his worst scowl that usually made Philippe want to laugh because he looked so funny.

But right now Philippe didn't have the tiniest laugh inside him. Anton said he should have skis. Mama finally agreed—and now Papa wouldn't even listen to the word. In fact, Papa was staring so hard at Philippe he wondered if Papa knew he was even just thinking of skis. Perhaps if Philippe made it a very small thought, just one to fill an odd corner, it wouldn't be so loud on his face.

But he couldn't. SKIS spread around and filled up every thought that he had, and he couldn't stop thinking!

Miserably Philippe hunched his brown head over his plate. They ate Mama's soup that simmered in a big pot on the stove and received little bits of everything only to give back a wonderful flavor and taste. But Papa was worrying about money; Anton was worrying about his truck;

Philippe was worrying about the only thing on his mind; Mimi was worrying about the soggy butter-flies and whether there would be a punishment. Mama worried about all the others worrying. It was a very quiet meal.

Afterwards Mimi wanted to go skiing again, but Philippe was no longer content with his barrel staves. "You go, Mimi," he said. "Those skis are too silly for anyone my age."

Mimi was so hurt that she went out to talk to Michele, the cow, who always seemed to understand no matter what age you were.

That made Philippe cross, because he wanted to go and see Michele himself. Instead, he stood by the front window and counted the cars and the people and the pairs of skis that drove by so gaily on the way to the inn. This made him feel so much worse that after a while he just lay on the floor with his eyes shut and pretended he was a famous skier about to take a dangerous run and break a world record.

Anton saw him and said, "Want to go to the ski inn? I'm taking some cabbages to the cook there."

"I guess so." Somehow the afternoon had become as flat as the morning had been exciting.

He helped Anton haul the green-curled cabbages, some bigger than his head, out of the cold cellar onto the truck.

They climbed in, and Anton started the motor, which shook and shivered and groaned and chattered like someone getting out of bed on a cold morning.

The plows had packed the snow so high along the roadway that it was like riding through a tunnel with shiny white sides and a blue ceiling.

"Would Papa really sell the hill?" Philippe asked.

"If he has to get more money to run the farm, that's as good a way as any," Anton explained. "Papa says the hill is a luxury, and we can still look at it no matter who owns it."

"But it just wouldn't feel the same," said Philippe sadly.

Anton's old truck looked very dim and worn as he drove by the bright cars parked in front of the inn. He backed up by the kitchen door, and Philippe helped him carry in the cabbages. The kitchen was as big as Philippe's whole house, and it had machines to wash dishes and mix cakes and peel potatoes. Even with all the machines pumping and whirring, there were a lot of people rushing

around, too. Philippe backed into a corner and stared while the head cook admired the cabbages and paid Anton.

"For a little farm you raise big things," he heard the man say. "How about some squash tomorrow?"

"Okay," said Anton. "If the truck holds out."

Just then a tall man with a deep tan stopped and spoke to Anton.

"Hello, Anton! I haven't seen you since last winter. Are you busy this year?"

"Not too busy," Anton said. "Mr. Vincent, this is my brother, Philippe."

Philippe looked up quickly, because he knew Mr. Vincent was the man who owned the inn.

Mr. Vincent slid his face around into a smile for Philippe, and then it slipped back quickly into the lines of a busy man.

"I wanted to ask you if you'd have time to be an instructor for some of the beginning skiers," he said.

"Oh!" Anton's voice sounded very thin and tight. "I'm not skiing any more. You remember that race I messed up—well, my leg hasn't been the same since. No strength in it."

Mr. Vincent's face grew sorry. "That is a shame. Why, we were all counting on you to make the Olympics in another year."

"I won't say I hadn't dreamed of it. Now, if there's any Olympic skiing, I guess Philippe will have to do it," Anton told him.

Philippe stared at his feet until they suddenly seemed twice as big. It made him uneasy to hear of a dream that hadn't come true, and he wished Anton wouldn't joke about his skiing.

But Mr. Vincent was looking hard at Anton.

"You don't think you could manage skis enough to teach beginners?"

"I haven't tried," said Anton rather shortly. "And the way things are now, I won't have time."

"If you change your mind, just let me know!" Mr. Vincent smiled earnestly at Anton and then hurried off.

When they were outside, Anton asked, "Do you want to look around?"

Philippe did, and Anton led him about until they came to the wide slopes where figures darted and sped about on skis.

The deep snow was packed down so that it was as smooth as a pavement, except for the holes people made when they fell down. Philippe was relieved to see that some sat down and picked themselves up as often as he had that morning.

The most exciting thing to him was the tow that pulled the skiers up the long slope. He watched a boy swing himself into one of the little chairs hanging down from a great cable, and rest his skis on the bar below.

"It must be fun to go up in that!" exclaimed Philippe. "Maybe someday I can."

Anton nodded. "Keep hoping," he said.

By now the boy in the red shirt was high up on the hill, growing smaller and smaller, until Philippe couldn't tell one tiny dot of a person from another. "This hill is higher and steeper than my hill," Philippe said to Anton.

"Your *hill!*" Anton laughed. "Well, I guess I thought of it as my hill, too, for a while. Anyway, this isn't a hill—it's a lower slope of a mountain. And just look at all those mountains beyond."

Philippe did. Snow-covered mountain slopes stretched as far as he could see. They looked very big and very lonely.

"That's where the real skiing is!" Anton said with a quiet longing in his voice that made

Philippe realize how much his brother minded not skiing any more. And seeing quite a few boys reminded Philippe of his two wishes—for more time to play and someone to play with.

"Let's go back and ride in the truck," Philippe said. Both of them standing there wishing began to hurt too much.

Philippe was in such a hurry to turn his back on it all that he bumped into a boy who stood uneasily by a pair of gleaming skis stuck in the snow.

But the boy barely noticed him. He was frowning at an older man beside him. "Look, Toby," the man was saying. "You'll never ski if you don't try."

"But I don't want to," the boy said.

Philippe's mouth dropped open. Imagine a boy having skis and not wanting to ski! It was too much! Philippe began to feel a little like Papa. Don't mention skis to him!

"Come on," Anton called, and they hurried toward the truck.

"Papa won't have to grumble about my truck drinking too much gas any more," Anton said sadly. "I don't think it's going to last much longer anyway. And then what will we do? The only money we take in now is on vegetables I haul over to the inn. I guess the best thing Papa can do is to sell the hill."

When Philippe went to bed that night, he felt uncomfortably full of things he wanted to do— with no way to do them. He wanted Anton to be able to ski again, and he wanted to find some way so Papa wouldn't sell his hill. Over and over they tumbled in his mind. They were both very grown-up problems, and Philippe couldn't think of any way to solve either of them. But he just had to do something.

The next morning Papa kept Philippe so busy filling the woodboxes for the kitchen stove and the parlor stove that he didn't have time to think. But in the afternoon there wasn't anything in particular for him to do.

The best place to think was on top of his hill, so he started to trudge up. The barrel-stave skis were stuck in a snowbank just where he had left them the day before. As long as he was going up, he might as well have a quick way down; so he picked up the skis and plodded slowly up the hill.

He had meant to take the silly butterflies off the elastic bands, but he was so busy worrying that he forgot about it. At the top he bent down and tucked his boots under the butterflies. The hill leaned away from him, and there at the bottom was his house, as small and far away as a picture post card.

Suddenly he wanted to see something different. He turned his stubby skis around and slid into the woods that climbed the back slope of his hill.

He hadn't gone very far when he saw a boy about his own age slipping and skidding through the trees. The boy's beautiful long, slender skis were as slim as a whistle. He wore heavy ski boots tucked neatly into shining harnesses. It was the same boy Philippe had bumped into the day before at the inn—the boy who didn't want to ski.

Philippe wanted to hide behind a tree to cover up his odd skis and his old rubber-bottomed boots and his clumsy sheep-lined jacket. But the other boy looked up and saw him.

"Halloo," he said. "Any good place to ski around here?"

Philippe thought proudly of his hill. "Back here," he said. "I'll show you."

"Thanks," said the boy. "Those trails around the ski inn are too hard for me. I just want a big open place to fall down in."

Philippe led him back to the top of his hill. "I'm Philippe Tourneau," he said. "That's my house down there, and this is my hill."

"It looks nice," the other boy said. "I'm Toby Winters and I live in New York. Do you live here all year round?"

Philippe nodded. Here he had been wishing for someone to play with, but suddenly all the things he thought of to say seemed very small and unimportant.

"It's nice, but it sure is lonely around here," Toby said.

They stood there for a minute, shifting uneasily on their skis.

"Well, they tell me if I don't try to ski I'll never learn." Toby grinned. "I'll bet you ski real well."

"Not very," Philippe admitted. "But my brother did. He might have made the Olympics if he hadn't been hurt."

Toby looked at him admiringly. "My father's a wonderful skier, too." Then he sighed. "But it gets discouraging trying to keep up to fathers or brothers when they want you to. I can't even stay within sight of mine."

Philippe grinned. Toby came from a very different world, but apparently he had some of the same problems. "I'll go first," he said, "just to show you where the best places are to fall down."

The boys climbed and skied and fell and slid and rolled until they were both hot and panting. As they came near the bottom of the hill some time later, Philippe saw that Anton was watching them.

"See us skiing!" called Philippe.

"I see you sliding around," Anton said, "but I don't see you skiing. You're letting your skis run you, and you ought to be running your skis."

Both boys slipped around until they stopped, and then they stared at him like puppies eager to chase a ball if someone would only throw it.

"Oh, well—come over here," Anton said.

"This is Toby," Philippe told him.

"Hello. Now the first thing is to know how to stop. And the easiest way is not to fall down. It's to snowplow." Anton became very serious. "You turn your skis inward so they act like brakes, and it makes you go slower and slower till you stop. Just try it."

Both boys pushed off down the slope and tried to point their skis in. Philippe's barrel staves were shorter and easier to manage than Toby's long ones.

"Make your knees and ankles work," Anton told them.

Toby laughed. "You sound like the instructor at the inn. He just shouts 'Bend zee knees' all the time and never says why."

"I'll show you why. Give me your skis, Philippe." Anton was so interested that he forgot about his weak leg. Surprised, Philippe kicked the barrel staves toward him, and Anton stuck his big boots under the butterflies. Slowly and patiently he showed them how bending their knees gave them more freedom of motion. He moved like a dancer—even though his feet were tied down—showing how they could take their weight off one leg and shift it to the other.

Then he flipped the skis back to Philippe. The two boys tried everything he showed them until their knees cracked and their ankles snapped.

"This is worse than horseback riding," Toby gasped.

"When do we ski?" Philippe asked.

"You mean run downhill?" Anton laughed. "That's enough lesson for one day. Go on up, only this time you'll know how to stop when you come down."

Up they trudged, and this time, as Philippe shot downward, it was fun to think that he was the master of his skis. They would do just what he told them to and glide to a stop fit for the Olympics.

But somehow his skis were as eager as he was, and before he could stop them, they ran across each other and pitched him headfirst into the snow.

There he stuck, as tight as a key in a lock! Anton and Toby had to pull him out.

"My!" gasped Philippe. "I thought skiing was going to be as easy as falling downhill, but you have to work real hard at it!"

Anton laughed. "You'd better sit down while you can still bend your knees. Come inside for some chocolate, and then we'll take Toby and the squashes over to the inn."

"Could I come tomorrow and ski with you again?" Toby asked Philippe when they left him at the inn.

"Sure!" Philippe's face glowed happily. At last someone wanted to be a friend and do things with him.

"And would you show us some more skiing?" Toby asked Anton.

"If I can," said Anton.

When the truck rattled back into the yard, Anton led Philippe into the woodshed. "As long as you're trying so hard to learn to ski with those —with your skis, you can at least have some good poles."

He reached behind some old boards stacked in the corner and pulled out a sturdy pair of steel poles with the wonderful shining little wheels and strong leather wrist straps on them.

"Oh!" breathed Philippe.

"For some reason my poles didn't break even if my leg and my skis did," Anton explained. "I didn't want to throw them away, and I didn't want to look at them either. But you take them, and give that old broom you've been using back to Mama."

"Oh, thank you, Anton!" Philippe carried them upstairs quickly before anyone could stop him, and that night he kept waking up and looking for

the poles, shining like silver in the moonlight. Now all Philippe needed was a good pair of skis. He made up his mind that he would earn them some way, though he didn't know how he was going to do it.

Toby came the next day. Philippe was already eagerly practicing on the hill, swinging the glorious poles Anton had given him as if he were going to jump over mountains with them. Philippe greeted Toby uneasily, wondering when he would say something about the butterfly-banded barrel staves —especially now that his poles were so grand. But Toby never did. He didn't even remark on the poles.

By the time they had skied for a while, Philippe forgot his uneasiness and felt as if he and Toby had been friends all their lives.

Each day Anton made them practice and practice all the things they had learned about skiing, and then he would show them a little more. Each day, too, Philippe noticed that Anton borrowed his brother's barrel staves a little longer and tried going farther on them.

The third day Anton made them practice going uphill on their skis with a step that is called the

herringbone, because it leaves a trail like the backbone of a fish. He plodded up the hill on Philippe's
skis, to show them how, and when they reached
the top, he stood looking longingly at the slope
below.

"Why don't you ski down?" Philippe asked.

Anton frowned at Philippe's funny skis. "I
don't know why you call it skiing on these things,"
he said crossly.

Philippe was hurt. Toby had never once men-
tioned how odd his skis were, and Philippe, now
that he had learned to manage them, was quite

fond of them. He was afraid Toby would laugh—
and if he did, Philippe would feel as if he had lost
a friend rather than found one.

But Toby didn't laugh. He just said, "Do you
want to use mine?"

Anton looked at the shining skis. "No—I might
break them." Then quickly he pushed himself off
with the poles and sped down the hill. Philippe
and Toby watched eagerly. Anton's flight looked
as easy as a raindrop running down a window-
pane! But when Anton tried to stop at the bottom, he fell. Philippe gasped! Suppose Anton
broke his leg again!

When his brother didn't move, Philippe ran
down the hill as fast as he could in the deep snow.

"Are you hurt?" he shrieked.

Anton looked surprised. "No—I don't think so.
I just haven't tried to get up."

Philippe tried to pull him up, but Anton was so
heavy it was like a rowboat trying to tug an ocean
liner.

"I was thinking that maybe if I skied every day
my leg might get stronger," Anton said eagerly.
"But right now I've got to fix the truck. Here are
your skis and poles."

By the time Philippe and Toby climbed up the hill once more, the sun was hurrying toward the mountaintops, ready to gild them with a tinsel-bright good-night gleam. The shadows of the trees began to reach out and stretch like a long yawn at the end of the day.

Toby looked at his wrist watch. "I'd better find my way back. I hope I can come again tomorrow. My father said we might go back to New York, but now that I've found someone to have fun with, I wish he'd stay longer."

"Will you come back next year?" asked Philippe anxiously.

"I'll sure try," Toby told him.

"I'll go along with you for a way," Philippe said. He admired Toby very much. He still hadn't said one thing about Philippe's butterfly-banded barrel staves!

Toby pushed off on his slim skis, and Philippe stubbed along behind him.

Suddenly Toby sailed down a steep place. There was a large tree right in front of him. "Whooooops!" shouted Toby.

Before he could stop, he whacked into the tree. His skis cracked with a splintering sound.

Toby fell back in a spray of snow and lay still.

Philippe scrambled along sideways down the slope and bent over him. "Toby! Toby!" he shouted. "Can you get up?"

The other boy's eyelids moved slightly, and he whispered, "It's my leg. Broken, I guess. Get my father at the inn——"

Philippe slid his sheep-lined jacket under Toby's head and shoulders and unwound his gray wool scarf and covered as much of Toby as he could with it. "I'll be as quick as I can," he promised.

The tracks Toby made as he came from the inn each day sank down and down between the trees. Philippe slipped and slid. He wanted terribly to walk, but the skis were faster! If he could just manage them instead of the skis managing him.

Trees whooshed past him. The trail bumped his knees up and down. It began getting steeper, and Philippe began to rush faster and faster. If it hadn't been for Toby, Philippe never would have tried such hard skiing all at once!

Suddenly he swooped out of the woods onto a wide cleared slope that plunged frighteningly off ahead of him. The setting sun made the windows of the ski inn leap out like gold flames at the foot of the hill. Philippe barely had time to realize where he was, his skis kept him so busy. He balanced as best he could and just hoped and hoped he wouldn't fall as he zipped and wavered nearer and nearer the inn.

He called out to the few other skiers on the slope, but they were all rushing toward the inn and

a warm fireside, and the wind tossed his shouts away like old autumn leaves.

One minute Philippe was still flying, the cold air whistling through his thin sweater and shirt. The next minute, thud! there he was on his back with

his feet waving the barrel staves for all the world to see! But he looked up and found that at least he had reached the bottom and that there were two men hurrying over to pick him up.

Philippe sat up and then tried to stand up. Whew! The whack on his head when he fell made him dizzy.

One of the men scooped him onto his feet. "All right?" Philippe saw it was Mr. Vincent.

"Yes," Philippe panted. "I'm all right. I want to find a Mr. Winters."

"I'm Winters," the other man said excitedly. "You haven't seen my boy, have you?"

"Yes. He fell up on the hill, and his leg is broken."

"We'll get the ski patrol," Mr. Vincent said.

In a few minutes two ski patrolmen came running with their packs full of first-aid things and a toboggan for a stretcher. Mr. Winters clamped his skis on and was impatient to be off.

"Can you show us where Toby is?" he asked Philippe.

"Yes." Philippe untangled his barrel staves and blushingly stuck his boots under the poor tired felt butterflies. He felt as if he were out in the hot summer sun, he was so red with embarrassment. Why, oh, why couldn't he have come gliding down to the rescue, a hero on shining hickory skis!

Mr. Vincent suddenly stared at him. "Did you come all the way down that slope on those—those skis?"

"Yes." Philippe started shuffling off after the ski patrol. But he felt a warm pat on his shoulder.

"You're quite a skier!" Mr. Winters said. "I wish my Toby could do as well."

"Oh, but he can!" Philippe said. "He's been skiing on my hill for three days, and my brother Anton has been teaching him. He went all the way down this afternoon without falling once!"

"Is it that nice open hill with a house and barn at the bottom?" Mr. Vincent asked, while they waited for the ski tow to start.

"Yes."

"I've been looking at it. We want a good slope for beginners. Your father wouldn't rent us the hill and barn in the winter, would he?"

Philippe's face spread into an allover grin! "I'm sure he would!" he exclaimed. He wouldn't mind sharing his hill, just as long as they wouldn't have to sell it.

"And if Anton is skiing again, maybe he'd give lessons on the hill. You tell your father and brother I'll be over in the morning. Now, young man——"

Philippe found himself lifted into the chair of the tow, his skis resting on the bar beneath it. The ski patrolmen were already in their places, with the toboggan strapped to another chair.

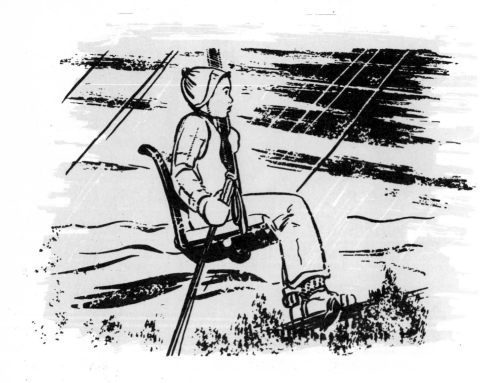

Smoothly the tow started to move. Philippe sailed through the air while the ground and then the treetops fell away underneath him. Without his sheep-lined jacket Philippe shivered, but it was fun. He had never thought that he would be riding the ski lift! Now he was really flying through the air. Just wait till he told Mimi how it felt!

When his little chair swooped in by a platform on the hill, the ski patrolmen grabbed him off, while his chair sailed away without him.

Mr. Winters and Mr. Vincent slid off the tow, and with flashlights they started through the trees. Philippe felt lost. It was so strange with the beams of light poking and prodding the snow and woods. But he found his tracks and in a few minutes led them to where Toby lay.

"Here he is!" Philippe called. They bent over the boy, who smiled but didn't try to say anything except "Thanks" to Philippe.

When Toby was on the toboggan and the blankets were wrapped around him, all set for the run downhill, Philippe picked up his jacket and scarf.

"Would you like to come back to the inn and get warm and dry?" Mr. Winters asked.

"No, thanks. I don't want to ski down that slope again tonight." Philippe shivered at the thought.

"Well, take a flashlight," Mr. Vincent said. "We don't want two boys with broken legs!"

So Philippe picked his way through the trees until he came to his own side of the hill.

Philippe stood there a moment, thinking of how the hill had been his very own world. It wouldn't feel like his own hill any more, with so many people skiing on it. But he certainly had had much more fun sharing the hill with Toby than he had ever had alone on it. Maybe it would be a better and more exciting world for him from now on.

Then down he flew, from the very top of the hill, with the little beam of light dancing around before him as if a tiny moon were skipping for joy.

Philippe felt as if he had another moon inside him, he was so alight with happiness. What a lot he had to tell Mama and Papa and Anton and Mimi at supper! And at the bottom Philippe slowed down and made his skis stop just where he wanted them to. That was the biggest surprise of the day!

When he kicked them off, he was going to stuff them into the nearest snowbank. But now that they had carried him safely through such an adventure, he began to feel very fond of them.

He took them into the kitchen and put them to dry by the stove.

"Anton!" he announced, "I can really ski now. I stopped my skis when I wanted to, and I went all the way down the slope to the ski inn—and that's steep!"

"All the time I thought you were in the back yard!" gasped Mama. "My, it's nice you don't know about some things until they've come out all right."

"Why were you at the ski inn?" asked Anton.

So Philippe told them. Mama stood at the stove and forgot to ladle the food. Anton was so surprised that Philippe had gone down such a steep hill that he just listened without saying a thing. Mimi thought it was a wonderful adventure —but she did wish she'd been with him. Papa was so amazed that he forgot to remind Philippe not to mention skis.

Everyone was so excited that they all forgot to eat until Mama said, "Supper is growing colder and colder. But cold food won't hurt warm hearts, I guess. You've been a brave boy, Philippe, and Papa and Anton and Mimi and I are all very proud of you."

Then Philippe came to the most exciting thing of all. "Papa, you won't have to sell the hill. Mr. Vincent wants to rent it and the barn in the winter so people can learn to ski on it. And, Anton, he says if you're skiing again, maybe you'd teach the classes."

"Have you been skiing?" Mama pounced at Anton with a hard look that made him feel as if he were back at Philippe's age.

"Yes. I guess all my leg needed was some exercise. It feels fine now." Anton smiled. "I guess I'll go see Mr. Vincent in the morning."

"He's coming here to see you and Papa and the hill," Philippe told them. "You will rent the hill, won't you, Papa? But you won't sell it!"

Papa smiled. "I guess letting them rent it will make this a pretty unusual place. There aren't many farms where you can make the land work for you all year round."

Papa wouldn't sell the hill! Philippe felt as if a large dent in his heart had been straightened out and he were whole and happy again. And he felt very grown-up, too, because he had solved a hard problem. Even his three wishes seemed to have taken care of themselves.

Toby was a real friend, even if Philippe might not see him again until next year. With lots of people around skiing he wouldn't have time to wish he had time to play. He expected to be very busy. Surely there were some things he could do to help. And now that his skis were heroes, too, it didn't matter quite so much that he didn't have the right kind. Still, it would be nice——

Anton must have been thinking the same thing. "Now, Papa," he said, "you surely ought to get Philippe some good skis!"

"What about you?" Papa asked. "Are you going to teach skiing on Philippe's? You're the one who needs the skis."

"If you rent the hill, Gaston, you can get us all skis. Maybe you and I ought to try again, too. If our knees will still bend," said Mama.

"One at a time," said Papa. "Anton first because he needs them. Philippe next, if things work out right. You and me and Mimi—well, maybe Philippe would make us some barrel-stave skis!"

"But not with my butterflies!" begged Mama.

Philippe smiled dreamily. The heat of the kitchen was slowly making him sleepy. Someday, Papa had promised, he would have those shining skis. It was too nice a thought to fall asleep over. He went into the front parlor, where it was cold enough to wake him up around the edges of his mind. He thought delightedly about SKIS.

The next morning Philippe was so tired from his adventure that he just lay in bed for a long time admiring the hill through his window. Suddenly he saw four men tramping up it. There were Papa and Anton. He hopped out of bed and danced up and down in his bare feet because the floor was too cold to stand on. But he had to see if it was Mr. Vincent and Toby's father, too. It was! He was missing something!

Philippe put on his clothes so fast that he was quite breathless when he ran into the kitchen and reached for his outdoor clothes.

"Wait a minute!" said Mama.

"I want to hear what they say about my hill." Philippe was already struggling into his jacket.

"Wait a minute. The hill will be there a long, long time. And there's something here you might want to see first."

"Where?" Philippe looked around in such a hurry that he looked like a top spinning.

Mimi giggled. "Look where you left your skis to dry."

Philippe looked and blinked and looked again.

Winking and gleaming in the sunlight was a tall, slender pair of glistening new hickory skis.

They had shining steel spring bindings and handsome leather straps.

"Read the tag!" Mimi shrieked.

Philippe bent over and picked up the tag. But first he ran his hand admiringly along the clean, swift wood. The tag read, "For Philippe from Toby. Here's hoping these skis will carry you faster than a butterfly."

What a beautiful pair of skis! What a good friend Toby was! Philippe gave a happy sigh.

"I guess I'll take my skis out," he said, "and try flying down our hill."

Think It Over

1. Most of us have a special or favorite place. Philippe's favorite place was the hill behind his house. Tell how he felt about "his hill."
2. When Philippe climbed to the top of his hill to dream, he wished for three things. What were they?
3. What made Philippe decide that he could not get his skis by wishing and that he would have to find a more practical way to get them?
4. Tell what Philippe did and how he did it.
5. What were the two very grown-up problems that Philippe wished he could solve?
6. Who had an accident and how did Philippe help?
7. What is a ski patrol?
8. Name two good things that happened as a result of Toby's accident.
9. How did Philippe feel when he found out that Papa would not have to sell the hill?
10. What were some of the things in this story that made you happy?
11. Do you think *Philippe's Hill* would have been a good story without Toby's gift to Philippe? Give the reasons for your answer.

Painting Pictures

The author paints many pictures with words. Try to make an actual painting of the word pictures below for your notebook.

1. The hill leaned away from him, and there at the bottom was his house, as small and far away as a picture post card.
2. The shadows of the trees began to reach out and stretch like a long yawn at the end of the day.
3. Then down he flew, from the very top of the hill, with the little beam of light dancing around before him as if a tiny moon were skipping for joy.

The Magic of Words

Turn to the page given after each sentence to see how the author said the same thing in a more interesting way. Then write all the sentences as they appear in the book.

1. Mr. Vincent smiled. (page 214)
2. The noisy wind drowned his shouts. (page 236)

3. Philippe's eyes were bright with eagerness. (page 206)
4. But Anton didn't notice that Papa was getting mad. (page 208)
5. By the time Philippe and Toby climbed up the hill once more, the sun was about to set behind the mountaintops. (page 232)
6. He went into the front parlor where it was cold and he could think. (page 251)

More Books to Read

FITZSIMMONS, ROBERT. *How to Ski.*
Garden City: Doubleday & Company, Inc., 1964.
Easy lessons in skiing for the beginner.

PETRIDES, HEIDRUN. *Hans and Peter.*
New York: Harcourt, Brace & World, Inc., 1962.
A story written by a fifteen-year-old Dutch girl about two little boys who succeed in building their dream house.

KINGMAN, LEE. *Pierre Pidgeon.**
Boston: Houghton Mifflin Company, 1943.
Pierre Pidgeon earns a dollar to buy a ship model in a bottle, but he has bad luck with it. You will be interested to learn what happens.

*Included in *Invitations to Personal Reading*, Curriculum Foundation Classroom Library, Scott, Foresman and Company.

Jesse Stuart has lived all his life in the Kentucky hills. His love for the mountains and mountain people shows through in the many books, short stories, and poems he has written.

When the author was small, his family was very poor, and frequently he had to work instead of going to school. He managed to graduate from high school, however, and then worked his way through college. Because he felt education was so important in giving him a chance in life, Jesse Stuart has been a teacher for many years.

Five of his books are written for children, and you will probably want to read some of them after finishing *A Penny's Worth of Character*. They are all about life in the Kentucky mountains.

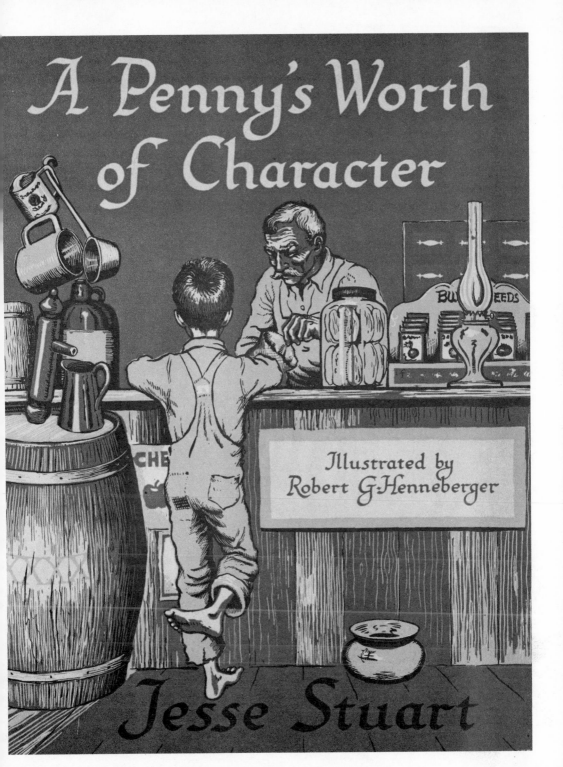

A Penny's Worth of Character

Illustrated by
Robert G. Henneberger

Jesse Stuart

A Penny's Worth of Character

by JESSE STUART

Illustrated by ROBERT HENNEBERGER

Whittlesey House
McGRAW-HILL BOOK COMPANY
New York · Toronto · London

Summer in the Kentucky mountains
is a very beautiful time. This is
especially true when you are about
eight years old and every tree has
a story to tell and every stream is
full of adventure.

This book is the story of a summer
day when Shan let his desire for a
lemon soda pop and a chocolate bar
lead him into making a decision that
changed his whole world for a while.

You'll want to think about what Shan
did and decide whether you would
have done the same thing. You'll
also want to find out how Shan's
mother helped him discover his
lost happiness.

A Penny's Worth of Character by Jesse Stuart
Illustrated by Robert Henneberger
Copyright 1954 Jesse Stuart and Robert Henneberger
Used by permission of the Publisher, McGraw-Hill Book Company

Contents

Shan's Mother Calls

"Shan, I want you to go to the store for me this morning," his mother said. "I've got a list made out of things I need."

Shan's mother, Millie Shelton, was doing the family wash before the sun got high enough to shine down into the deep, green valley. When the sun got high, the day grew warmer and the flowers wilted on their stems. Then it was almost too hot to rub clothes on a washboard over a tub of warm, soapy water.

"Mom, you got some eggs for me to take to Mr. Conley?" Shan asked.

"Not this morning," she replied. "Our hens aren't laying too well this time of year. We're not getting more eggs than we need for ourselves."

Shan was disappointed. When Shan carried eggs to the store, there were always a few pennies left over after he'd traded the eggs for groceries. His mother let him have these extra pennies to buy candy.

Shan was always happy if there were as many as three pennies left over. He bought peppermint sticks and gumdrops with these.

Sometimes there was a whole nickel left over, and then he bought his favorite chocolate bar. And sometimes—rarely—there was a dime left to buy the chocolate bar and a lemon soda pop, too. He ate the chocolate bar and drank his lemon soda pop at the same time. The two were so good together that when he thought about them he got hungry. He had never tasted anything better in his life than a chocolate bar when he had a cool lemon soda pop to wash it down.

His mother noticed his disappointment. "Shan, there is a pile of empty sacks in the smokehouse," his mother said. "You can trade them for candy. Don't take the one over on the right by itself—it has a hole in the bottom of it. I'll probably be able to use that one for peaches."

"Thanks, Mom. I'll get them."

He began to smile as he thought of the candy he would get at Mr. Conley's store.

Shan ran to the smokehouse and opened the door. He hurried in and found the sacks stacked up neatly on a chair. There were more than he expected. He counted one, two, three, four, five, six, seven, eight—and very slowly he counted the ninth sack. He had hoped there would be ten. Ten large sacks equaled a dime. And with a dime he could get his favorite chocolate bar and lemon soda pop.

Shan stood there thinking. Then he went over and looked at the tenth sack with a hole in it. It sure was too bad this sack had a hole in it.

Shan Makes a Decision

He tiptoed to the smokehouse door and looked out to see where his mother was. She was walking across the yard with another basket heaped high with clothes. She was taking them to the clothesline. The clothesline was on the other side of the yard from the smokehouse. He waited until she set the basket down and started pinning up the clothes. Then he put the nine sacks under his arm and started out.

He stopped; then he went back. He picked up the tenth and looked at the hole. "Not really much of a hole," he said to himself. "A pretty useful old sack if you didn't put stuff like sugar or meal into it."

He knew how Mr. Conley took the top sacks from the pile and held them up to the lighted window and looked inside to see if any light came through. But Mr. Conley was old, and he might not be seeing too well. And besides, Mr. Conley never looked at all the sacks. He might look at some on the top and some on the bottom of the pile, but he wouldn't hold every one in the pile up to the light.

Suddenly Shan knew the way to fool Mr. Conley. He put a good sack down. This was number ten. Then he laid down number nine and number eight. These were good sacks, too. Then he put the sack with a hole in it down for number seven. He placed six good sacks on top. This would throw Mr. Conley off either way he looked. If he looked at the sacks from the top or the bottom, it wouldn't matter now.

Shan smiled as he picked up the paper sacks and held them under his arm. His troubles were over. He had found the way to get what he wanted. He could have both the chocolate bar and the lemon soda, and shucks, what did one little old hole amount to? He walked through the door and stepped onto the soft green grass.

"What's kept you so long?" his mother asked.

"Mom, I've been counting the sacks," he said.

"The basket is on the kitchen porch, and I have my list in the bottom of the basket," she told him. "Hurry, Shan. There are things on the list I need now. Don't fool along talking to the birds and wading in the creek hunting crawdads and minnows."

"I won't, Mom," he said.

Shan ran and got the split-white-oak basket his mother had made to carry groceries in. The list was in the bottom of the basket where the wind couldn't blow it away.

Old Rags, Shan's black-and-white hound, walked over and whined as if he were trying to speak.

"You can't go with me, Rags," Shan said. "I'm going to the store."

"Hurry now, Shan," his mother said. "Never mind the hound. And don't fool along talking to turtles, terrapins, and young rabbits."

Shan walked around the big log house. He walked past the chimney made of many-colored stones that somebody in years gone by had picked up from the fields. Now the morning-glories that his mother had planted climbed up the chimney. There were many colors of blossoms—blue, white, and purple—and they were shaped like little bells.

Shan stopped to look at the hen's nest hidden under the morning-glories in the chimney corner. Maybe the hen had laid an egg this morning. The hen that laid in this nest seldom missed laying an egg every day. But there was no egg this morning. If there had been, he thought, he might put the egg in his pocket. An egg would bring two cents, and if Mr. Conley found the sack with a hole in it, Shan would still be sure to get his chocolate bar and the lemon soda pop. To think of them made his steps grow faster. It was too bad that the hen hadn't laid this morning, he thought as he walked around to the front yard.

The World Belongs to Shan

Shan went through the gate toward The Valley road, and he stopped once to look back when a pewee flew over his head with something in her bill. She had made a nest of mud under the eaves. And there were young birds in that nest, too. Shan had heard them crying for food. Since he'd never been able to climb high enough to see, he'd often wondered how many young birds she had. He knew there were three young birds in the cardinal's nest. Shan loved the birds. He carried bread crumbs from the table and put them on top of the gateposts for the cardinals. But he didn't have time to watch them now, for he had to hurry to Mr. Conley's store to get things for his mother and for himself.

The morning was beautiful. Shan heard the songs of many wild birds hidden among the wild crab-apple trees on either side of The Valley. He knew that they were singing because they were as happy as he was. When he reached a big sycamore where people often sat to rest in the shade beside the road, he stopped again. There was a redheaded woodpecker holding on to a dead branch with his toes while he bored a hole with his long black bill. He made more noise than Shan's father made when he bored a hole into a plank with a brace and bit.

When the woodpecker saw Shan looking up at him, he stopped to look down at Shan. But he didn't stop very long. He went back to boring into the tree again. Then Shan remembered his father telling him that woodpeckers bored into dead trees to find worms. Shan's father had once shown him, when he was cutting stovewood with an ax, the kind of worms the woodpeckers bored into trees to get. They were little white worms with brown heads. The worms could eat their way into the trees, too. Shan thought it was strange what animals and birds liked to eat. He knew the woodpecker probably liked such things better than chocolate bars and lemon soda pop.

Between Shan's home and Mr. Conley's store there were three big trees where people stopped to rest themselves and their horses. One was the big sycamore where Shan had seen the redheaded woodpecker. The second one was a white oak with a bushy top and long branches that spread like a big green cloud brooding over the earth. Here people walking along the road would meet each other and sit under the green-cloud shade to talk.

Below this white oak was a hole of water, clear and blue, with wild phlox growing on the bank just across from the tree. Wild phlox couldn't grow on the side the tree was, for the tree's giant roots grew above the water. The stream had washed the dirt away from these roots. Shan saw something long

and white lying wrapped around one of the roots. He set his basket in the road and put his sacks into it. He found a rock and threw it down at the water snake. His rock hit the root and jarred the snake off into the water. It swam back under the roots of the tree. He's trying to get his breakfast, too, Shan thought. He's waiting there for the minnows to swim out so he can swallow one.

Shan stood there looking at the water and regretting he had missed the snake. He always tried to kill water snakes because they ate the minnows. He liked to throw bread crumbs into the water and watch minnows swim up and swallow them. He knew something else they liked, too. On the side of the white oak was a green fly. Shan tiptoed up and put his hand over the fly. He threw it down onto the water. Then he saw the minnows coming from under the bank on the other side of the stream. Their little silver bodies raced through the clear blue water, and the largest one beat the others and swallowed the fly. Shan caught more green flies until the minnows had had a good breakfast. Then he got his basket and sacks and hurried on. He knew he wasn't going to stop any more because his mother had told him to hurry.

Now the road and the creek came together. The water was very shallow. Here he had liked to ride in the wagon with his father and watch the horses' big feet splash the water. There was a path around the hill for the older people who wore shoes. But Shan liked to wade in the water. He wanted to feel the water flowing over his feet and around his legs. No wonder the minnows like the water, he thought. He knew it would be fun to be a minnow and swim in this clean blue water. He knew the minnows breathed water and drank air the way he breathed air and drank water. He'd like to try their way of life if it weren't for the snakes. There were these awful snakes that would be waiting to swallow him if he were a minnow.

As he waded down The Valley stream, he was careful not to splash water. He was afraid he'd get his paper sacks wet. If he splashed the sacks, Mr. Conley might go over them real close. And if he did, he might find the hole in number seven. Shan saw a flat rock lying on the slate bottom of the stream, and he pushed the rock with his toe. A crawdad came from under it. It swam backwards, pulling the water with its fan-shaped tail. It had a pair of little pinchers with pink ends, and raised

these up in the water when it swam. But Shan had caught crawdads with his hands and let them pinch him and they didn't hurt. With his big toe he pursued the crawdad to make him swim. Shan laughed as the crawdad swam backwards into the bank. He pushed more rocks lying on the slate as he waded down The Valley stream, which was also the road. Soon there were as many crawdads swimming backwards and crawling on the blue slate bottom as he had seen minnows in the deep hole under the white-oak shade. They were going in all directions, and now and then a minnow came upstream and hit Shan's bare leg under the water. This was a lot of fun, but he had to be careful not to splash his sacks.

Shan's Discovery

At the very spot where the road left The Valley stream and got back onto the dirt again, Shan saw a big brown-and-black checkered object with a long, black, scaly neck and a little bony head. It was resting on a sand bar. He knew better than to put his toe to its mouth. For this was a turtle, and it could bite.

He'd heard his father say that when a turtle bit anybody, it wouldn't let loose until it thundered or until the sun went down. As yet the sky wasn't very clear; still, it might be days before it thundered again. The sun wasn't shining in The Valley yet, and so it would be a long time before sunset. He didn't want the turtle to bite him, so he wouldn't give it a chance, but he did want to know what it was doing on the sand bar.

He walked over the dry sand that felt warm to his feet after he had waded in the cool water. He stopped a safe distance from the big turtle. The turtle turned its head sidewise and looked up at him with its bright, beady eyes. Shan wondered how it would feel to be able to hide in a shell. There were lots of things he wondered about this world he lived in. Animals and birds had different languages, and he wondered if they could understand each other. And they liked to eat different things and to eat each other. While he stood wondering about these things, the turtle started walking slowly across the sand bar.

On the spot where the turtle had been sitting, Shan discovered a small hole in the sand. He looked down into the hole and saw something white. He set his basket and sacks down again.

He put his hand down into the hole and fetched up five turtle eggs. He had often wondered where turtles laid their eggs. This was the first turtle's nest he had ever found. And slowly he put the eggs back into the hole in the sand.

He wondered why he had never found a turtle's nest before. Then he guessed that he had scared the old turtle from her nest before she covered her eggs with sand. That's the reason he'd not found turtles' nests. And he knew the sun on the sand warmed and hatched the eggs. Hens sit three weeks on their eggs and keep them warm to hatch young chickens. Not the turtles—they're smart, even if they do have little bony heads, Shan thought, covering the turtle eggs with sand for the old mother turtle he had scared from her nest.

Shan gathered his sacks under his arm and got his basket. He hurried down The Valley road that was winding and narrow under the shades of the tall willows and water birches. The road was sandy and soft to his feet. Shan had to hurry. He had seen so many interesting things and he had heard so many interesting sounds that he had stopped too many times. But he knew he wouldn't stop again.

Shan started running to make up for lost time. As he ran, he heard a wild scream. The scream came from a parent quail to warn one of its family that had strayed. The sun was coming down into this part of The Valley, and the parent quail had seen the shadow of a hawk as he glided down to get the young quail. Shan screamed, too, as he saw the Cooper hawk ready to pick up the baby quail in his claws. The hawk arose on fluttering wings, for he was frightened by Shan's voice, and the young quail was saved and got back to his parents.

Shan stopped a minute under a big sugar maple. This was the third big tree between his home and the store where neighbors met, rested, and talked. The bark of this tree was scarred. Each spring it was tapped to get the sap to make syrup. This was the biggest tree Shan had ever seen. It shaded more space than any tree he had ever been under. There were initials and dates carved over its body up as high as a tall man could reach. The grass was worn from under its shade. A gray lizard ran up the side of the tree. Shan watched him catch a fly. He was getting his breakfast, too. But Shan didn't have time to watch so many things. He knew he had to hurry.

As he ran again to make up for time he had lost, butterflies rose in small clouds from the touch-me-nots, buttercups, and phlox beside the road. They were pretty, fluttering clouds with all the colors of the rainbow. Shan heard the rain crows singing their mournful notes from the steep slopes above the road. They're begging for rain, Shan thought. He heard the songs of the cardinals, the chirruping of the ground sparrows, the cawing of crows, and once he heard the big *who-who* of a hoot owl that came from the tall timber. He heard the cries of the chicken hawks overhead. He saw a big hawk circling in the bright wind under the blue sky. The hawk was saying, *chickie-chickie-chickie*. Shan watched him circle high in the bright blue morning air. Then another hawk came flying straight from the tall timber, and the two hawks flew away together over the high walls of hills on the other side of The Valley. They're hunting their breakfast, Shan thought, remembering the lemon soda pop and the chocolate bar. Now he saw Mr. Conley's store, and he started running faster. He would soon be there.

Mr. Conley's Store

Mr. Conley's store stood where The Valley joined the Sandy River road. It was a little one-room building, painted white, under a grove of sycamore trees. Shan loved this store, and when he saw it, he always broke into a run to get there. He was as happy as he had ever been on this August morning when he stepped up the three steps into the store.

"Good morning, Mr. Conley," he said.

"Good morning, Shan," Mr. Conley greeted him.

Mr. Conley was standing behind the candy counter. Shan walked up and peeped through the glass to see if Mr. Conley had his favorite chocolate bars. They were under the glass all right. Shan counted six of them. He wished he had enough sacks to trade for all six.

"Gee, Mr. Conley, I was afraid you wouldn't have the chocolate bars," Shan said.

"Yes, Shan, those bars are mighty popular," he said. He walked from behind the counter.

Mr. Conley was a little man. He was bent with age.

"Have you brought me some sacks this morning, Shan?" he asked.

"Yes, I have," Shan replied.

"I'm glad you've brought them," Mr. Conley told Shan. "I need them now. I'm nearly out of large paper sacks. Customers buy flour and meal in small lots, and I've used all my sacks."

"I'm glad you want 'em, Mr. Conley," Shan said.

But Shan's heart pounded a little faster when Mr. Conley took the sacks from under Shan's arm.

"Got any holes in 'em?" Mr. Conley asked.

"You—y-y-y'd better see for yourself, Mr. Conley," Shan stuttered.

"I always examine them to see if there are any holes," Mr. Conley said.

Shan felt the blood rush to his face. And his heart pounded faster than it did when he was running down The Valley. Mr. Conley laid the paper sacks upon the counter. He took the first one and

held it toward the window. He opened the sack and looked inside.

"That sack's all right," Mr. Conley said. "When I hold one up against the light in the window and look in, if there's a hole big as a pinpoint, it will show big as a dime."

Shan didn't say anything. He couldn't think of anything to say. Even if he could have thought of anything, he couldn't have said it. His tongue felt as if it had been tied down with a twine string— the kind Mr. Conley used to wrap packages. Shan stood there silently as Mr. Conley lifted sacks two, three, four, and looked in.

"These are all right, Shan," he said. "I've not found a hole big as a pinpoint."

Then Mr. Conley picked up sack number five.

Surely he won't look at any more, Shan thought.

"This one is all right," Mr. Conley said as he laid it over with the other good ones.

Shan stood there hoping he wouldn't pick up another sack. But he watched Mr. Conley's small, nervous, white hand as it went down to pick up the sixth sack. Shan felt a warmer glow come over his face. And his heart pounded faster than ever while he watched Mr. Conley open the sack and look in.

"This one's all right," he said, and put that sack with the other good ones.

When Mr. Conley reached for the seventh sack, a box of cereal fell from the shelf.

"What was that?" Mr. Conley asked, turning to Shan.

"A box fell off the shelf," Shan murmured.

"I thought somebody had come in the store," Mr. Conley said as he turned back to the sacks. "But when a man gets seventy years old, his ears are not as good as they have once been. They get like an old paper sack that has been used so many times it's got holes in it!"

Shan looked up from the floor just in time to see Mr. Conley's little nervous hand go down for another sack.

Oh, I hope and pray he doesn't get that seventh sack, thought Shan.

Shan got his breath easier and his heart slowed down a bit when Mr. Conley took the last sack from the bottom. He lifted it up and looked inside.

Sweat ran in little streams down Shan's face now. Mr. Conley reached down and picked up sack number nine. There were only two sacks left. He held number nine and looked at it in a hurry. His hand went down again and rested on the eighth sack. That just left the sack with the hole in it.

"Shan, how many sacks did you bring?" he asked, turning around slowly and looking at Shan.

"T-t-ten, Mr. C-C-Conley," Shan stammered.

Mr. Conley counted slowly. "One, two, three, four, five." This was one pile. "Six, seven, eight, nine, ten."

Shan felt a great relief. Then Mr. Conley picked up the second pile and placed it on top of the first one. Shan knew that meant Mr. Conley would have just one good sack to use before he came to the bad one.

"I'll bet I know what you want for these sacks," Mr. Conley teased Shan as he walked toward the candy case. "You want chocolate bars."

"One chocolate bar, Mr. Conley," he said. "And I want a lemon soda pop."

"All right, my boy," Mr. Conley said, taking slow steps to the candy case. "You'll have the lemon soda pop and the chocolate bar."

Shan's hand was still sticky where he had wiped his face. And when Mr. Conley gave him the chocolate bar, it stuck to his hand. Then Mr. Conley took a cold lemon soda pop from the icebox. He opened the bottle and gave it to Shan. The ice-cold bottle felt good in his hot hand.

"Did your mother send for anything, Shan?" Mr. Conley asked. "I see you fetched a basket."

"Yes, sir," he replied. "The list is in the bottom of the basket."

Shan turned the bottle up to his mouth. He was in a big hurry to taste again his favorite drink. He swallowed and tasted, and then he looked at the bottle. It was lemon soda pop, but it didn't taste like the others he'd got at Mr. Conley's. It wasn't as good as the others had been. Then he took a bite from his chocolate bar. It had a funny taste, too. It didn't taste as good as the other chocolate bars Mr. Conley had sold him. He looked at the wrapper; it was the same kind of chocolate bar he had been getting. He looked around to see where Mr. Conley was. He was reading the list Shan's mother had sent.

Shan took another bite from the chocolate bar.

Then he followed it with a cool drink of his soda pop. That's the way he had always done. He'd eaten one and drunk the other, and the two were wonderful together. But they weren't so good now.

There was something funny about the taste of both. He took another bite of the chocolate bar and another drink of soda pop. He was in a hurry because Mr. Conley had filled the basket and was fetching it to him. Then Mr. Conley might go back to the sacks. He hurried to finish the chocolate bar, and he almost choked. But he washed the bite down with another drink of soda pop.

"I have everything your mother wanted, Shan," Mr. Conley said, setting the basket down on the counter.

Shan hated to leave any lemon soda pop in the bottle. He put the bottle to his lips while Mr. Conley stood there watching him. He couldn't swallow the last drink. He choked, and the soda pop almost strangled him. He set the bottle on the counter and grabbed his basket and ran from the store. Mr. Conley stood shaking his head as Shan ran out the door and down the steps. The fresh air outside the store was better for Shan. Still, he didn't feel just right as he began running up The Valley road for home.

A Penny's Worth of Character

"Shan, what happened to that flour sack with a hole in the bottom?" his mother asked as soon as he reached home.

She stood before him and pointed a finger. There was a frown on her face.

"Answer me, Shan," she said as she took the basket from his hand.

Shan moved his bare feet restlessly over the stone doorstep. He looked down at his feet, for he couldn't look up at his mother.

"Did you take that flour sack down to Mr. Conley's store?" she asked him again.

"Yes, Mom," he replied.

"I thought I told you not to take it!'

"You did."

"Then why did you do it?"

"I don't know."

"Did Mr. Conley go over the sacks to see if any had holes in 'em?" his mother asked.

"Yes, he did," Shan said.

"Why didn't he find the hole in that sack?" she then asked him.

"He didn't look through all of 'em," Shan said.

"You're lucky," she said. "But didn't you know it was wrong to do this? Didn't you know you were cheating Mr. Conley for a penny?"

"Yes, Mom," he said.

"Then why did you do it?"

"I wanted a dime, Mom," he said. "If I had taken nine sacks, I would have had only nine cents. I wanted a chocolate bar and a bottle of lemon soda pop. That took a dime."

"You know I never taught you to do a thing like this, don't you?" his mother said.

And then she didn't say another word. She turned and walked back through the house with the basket. Shan's thoughts spun around and around and over and over in his head, for he wondered what his mother was going to do now. He didn't have long to wait to find out what it was. She came back immediately with a new sack.

"Let this be a lesson to you," his mother said. "Take this sack to Mr. Conley to replace the no-good one. Tell him just what happened."

"Oh no, Mom," he said, "I—I—can't——"

"You *will*," she said firmly.

"Won't you just whip me and let me stay here?" he begged, beginning to cry. "I don't want to tell Mr. Conley what I've done."

"Go back and make things right," his mother said. "You will think before you ever do this again."

Shan looked up at his mother, and his eyes were filled with tears.

"I want to say one more thing, Mom," he said. "It's just one sack that's only worth a penny."

"One penny or a hundred pennies, Shan, the principle is the same," his mother said. "Do you remember that story your teacher told you about Abraham Lincoln when he was working in the store? He made a mistake of just a couple of pennies when he was giving a woman her change. Abraham Lincoln walked miles after a hard day's work to return them to her. That's how important it was to him. It made him feel better inside. Make you feel better, too."

Shan stood before his own front door crying. He didn't want to go back.

"Dry your tears," his mother told him. "Be on your way!"

There wasn't anything for Shan to do but turn and go back to the store, carrying one little light paper sack. The sack was only worth a penny, and he had a mile to walk there and back. As he walked down the road with the sack under his arm, he turned and looked back to see what his mother was doing. She was standing at their front door watching him walk slowly under the August sunlight down the hot, dusty road.

The Road Back

Earlier in the morning, when Shan had gone to the store with his ten sacks, the world had belonged to him. But now it was different. He walked under a hot sun down the dusty road, and this world didn't belong to him. This was a world he didn't want. When he reached the giant sycamore where he had watched the big redheaded woodpecker early that morning boring for worms, he stopped long enough to look up to see if the bird was back again, for it would soon be time for lunch. But the woodpecker had gone, and the dead limb looked hot and dry in the August sunlight. He wondered where the woodpecker had gone and if he was in a cool nest

301

in some hollow tree with his family of young birds away from the hot sun.

Beyond the sycamore, he walked over sand that was hot to his feet. The buttercups, over which the honeybees and bumblebees were humming two hours ago, were dry and wilting in the heat.

When Shan reached the big white oak, he wondered if bees and birds sweated as he did. He thought the birds didn't, for when the sun got hot, he never saw many birds—they were always in the cool shade. They gathered food in the morning when it was cool. He looked over the steep bank by the white oak at the deep water hole. The minnows weren't swimming around either. He saw them resting down there in the shaded water. A lazy minnow swam up, expecting Shan to throw a cracker crumb or a green fly, but Shan didn't—he didn't have time. And the minnow wasn't as pretty as it had been that morning when Shan felt the world belonged to him. He'd let the minnows find their own food. He had to work to get his. Look what the chocolate bar and the soda pop had cost him! He wasn't through yet. Look what a time he was having. Besides, his bare feet were hot from walking over the sun-baked sand.

When he waded into the stream, he touched a rock with his foot, and a crawdad came out swimming backwards. Shan didn't stop to watch it swim. He waded under the willow shades where the water was cooler to his feet. But he was careful not to splash water on the good sack he was carrying. He knew he had to give that to Mr. Conley. And he had to tell him about the sack with the hole in it. He dreaded to do that, too. He hoped there wouldn't be any customers to hear him.

When Shan walked over the sand bar, he didn't stop. He walked on and dried the tears from his eyes the best he could with the back of his hand. The turtle that had come to the sand bar to lay her eggs that morning was somewhere under the cool shade of the alder and the willow beside the stream.

Leaves on the big sugar maple were wilted, too. The hawks were no longer circling in the high blue sky. Shan walked slowly down the dusty road beyond the maple, thinking about Mr. Conley and the sack. He wondered what he would say when he gave it to him. He didn't want to take this sack to Mr. Conley.

Shan thought of running away from home. He thought about taking to the hills and going in any

304

direction that would take him from home. Then he wondered how he could leave his father. His father didn't have any part in making him take the sack back and explain to Mr. Conley why he was bringing it back. And he thought about how hard it would be to stay away from his baby brother and his little sisters. Shan wanted to make his mother feel sorry for sending him back to the store with a sack worth a penny.

But there wasn't anything left for him to do but to face Mr. Conley. To think of returning this sack made his face get hotter than the sun could make it. He tried to think of what he was going to say. But his tongue got heavy again. It was as lazy as the wind and didn't want to speak these words. It would only be a few minutes. He couldn't tell his heart to beat slower, and he couldn't keep his face from getting hotter.

He walked around the bend in the road where the cliffs looked up to the hot blue sky. This was the first time in Shan's life he hadn't wanted to see Mr. Conley's little white store under the sycamore trees. Always before, when he had walked around the winding road beneath these cliffs and seen the store, he had started running to get there. He saw two horses, with saddles on, hitched to the syca-more limbs. There was a team of horses hitched to a wagon standing in front of the store. Shan thought, People are in the store and they will hear what I have to tell Mr. Conley. I'll wait until they leave before I give him this sack.

Making a Wrong Right

Shan stopped outside and looked in. There were three men inside. Tom Eversole picked up his basket of groceries and walked out. Then Shan walked softly inside and listened to Mr. Conley count the eggs Manuel Greene had brought. He watched Manuel Greene trade his eggs for groceries. He stood in the back of the store so quietly they didn't see him. Then Manuel Greene put his basket of groceries on his arm and left the store. Only Tom Crum was left. He asked Mr. Conley for a sack of meal and flour. Mr. Conley picked up the sack on top and filled it full of meal from the barrel. He weighed it to see if he had ten pounds. He had eleven pounds, and he slowly dipped a pound out, watching his scales to see that it was correct. Shan watched, too.

Then Mr. Conley got the second sack. He dipped a scoop of flour from the barrel into the sack. Then he dipped another and another as if he were in a hurry. Shan saw the flour stream through the corner of the sack like water pouring through the holes in a sieve.

"Woops," Mr. Conley shouted as he put the sack down on the floor as quickly as he could to save the flour.

"Tom, did I tear that sack?" Mr. Conley said, looking up at Tom Crum.

"Don't think you did," Tom replied.

"I just bought this sack about three hours ago from Shan Shelton," he said. "He brought me ten sacks, and I looked at nearly all of 'em to see if there were any holes."

Shan was standing behind Mr. Conley and Tom Crum, and they hadn't seen him yet.

"These are the first sacks I've used today," Mr. Conley said. "See what it has cost me because I didn't look inside the other two sacks."

"You can't trust young 'uns nowadays," Tom Crum said. "They're not raised right."

309

"Nope, I don't guess you can," Mr. Conley said. "But I'd miss 'em if they didn't come in here and trade me sacks, roots, herbs, eggs, and pelts for candy and soda pop. I like to have 'em around the store."

When Mr. Conley had finished saying these words, he looked back and saw Shan with an empty sack in his hand. He looked straight at Shan. Tom Crum turned around to look.

"Want something, Shan?" Mr. Conley said to him.

"Yes," Shan said.

He walked up, his heart beating faster and the sweat running from his face. He gave Mr. Conley the sack.

"Just one?" Mr. Conley said.

"Yes," Shan said as Mr. Conley opened the sack to look for holes.

"No use to look for a hole in that one," Shan said.

"Oh," Mr. Conley said; then he laughed as he started to open his candy case.

"No candy for that one, Mr. Conley," Shan said.

"Why, what do you mean?" Mr. Conley asked. "Don't you want the penny?"

"I brought it because——" Shan couldn't finish saying what he wanted to tell Mr. Conley. His tongue was heavier than the wilted pods of leaves hanging over the hot road.

"You've got a good mother," Mr. Conley said.

Shan hadn't told Mr. Conley it was his mother who had sent him back with the sack. He wondered how Mr. Conley knew.

He remembered the thoughts he had had about his mother. He remembered thinking of running away from home to make her feel sorry because she had made him bring the good sack to Mr. Conley.

"There'll be a reserved seat in heaven for your mother," Mr. Conley said as Shan wiped the tears from his eyes with the back of his hand.

"You'll always be thankful when you grow up your mother made you do this, Shan," Tom Crum said as he rubbed his big rough hand over his beardy face. "This is a lesson in honesty you won't forget. It gives you a good foundation from your fingertips to your toes!"

"Mr. Conley, I'll bring you more sacks to pay for the flour you lost." Shan sobbed and turned to leave the store.

"Since you've been so honest, Shan," Mr. Conley said, smiling, "your debt is paid. I didn't lose much flour. And I think more of you than I have ever thought in my life."

Shan ran from the store. Mr. Conley said something to Tom Crum. Shan didn't hear what he said. He didn't want to hear, for it didn't matter now. The warm, lazy wind felt so good to his face. The air was as good and fresh to breathe as it had been when the dew was on the buttercups. The lazy wind dried the flow of tears that had come to his eyes in the store. These were tears he had tried to hold back.

Shan felt as light as a June bug in the August wind. He knew now how Abraham Lincoln felt after he had returned the pennies. Something had left him, and he started running up The Valley road for home. The blue sky above him was as beautiful as he had ever seen it. A redbird chirruped lazily from a cluster of pawpaws, and its chirruping was more beautiful than its spring song before an April shower. A hawk sailed over in the lazy wind, and it was pretty, too. Shan didn't fear anything now. His mother had been right when she said he would feel better within. How did she know all these things? He knew now that his mother was smart and good.

The turtle was back on the sand bar, and Shan ran up to her. She put her head back and went into her shell. "She's done that so I can pet her!" Shan shouted to the wind. "She knows I've heard that once she bit a person, she wouldn't let loose until it thundered or the sun went down!" Shan gently stroked her hard back.

Then he ran on because it was past his lunchtime. He could tell by the sun, for he could step on the head of his shadow. He was hungry, too. He ran into the water again, splashing it in all directions the way the big feet of one of his father's horses did. The beautiful crawdads must have thought he was a horse, for they came from under their little rock houses. They swam backwards, in all directions. They were beautiful again to Shan as they pulled the water with their fan-shaped tails. In the cool waters under the alder and willow shades, the minnows swam like arrows of flying silver.

Shan looked down and saw himself in the mirror of sky-blue water, and he was smiling. No one could tell by looking at his eyes now that he had ever cried. He had never been so happy. And the whole world was happy because he was. His world had never been so beautiful before, and it belonged to him again.

"Hello, Mom," he called to his mother as he came near the house. "I'm home."

Five W's

1. *Why* did Shan like to go to the store?
2. *What* did Shan do that he was later ashamed of?
3. *When* did Shan make his first mistake?
4. *Where* in the story did you first realize that Shan was unhappy about what he had done?
5. *Who* showed Shan how to make things right with his world?

Think It Over

1. What are some differences between the store where Shan went and the one where you go?
2. What did Shan take to Mr. Conley's store to trade for pennies? What do you sometimes take to the store to exchange for money?
3. What could you see, hear, and feel as you went along The Valley road with Shan?
4. Which of these would you see on *your* way to the store? What would you probably see that Shan did not?
5. Why do you think the lemon pop and chocolate bar didn't taste the same on this day as they had before?

6. What story did Shan's mother tell him about Abraham Lincoln and the pennies?
7. Describe Shan's second trip to the store. How was it different from the first?
8. When Shan returned from the store the second time and called, "Hello, Mom, I'm home," do you think he had changed any? How?
9. In *Skippack School* you read about some old beliefs. What old beliefs or superstitions did you find in this book?

Did You See?

When you read *A Penny's Worth of Character*, you may have seen some ways in which Shan's and Eli Shrawder's experiences were alike. Read the following sentences. Then copy the sentences in your notebook. If a sentence is true, put T after it. If a sentence is false, put F after it.

1. Both Eli and Shan lived on farms.
2. Both boys had mothers who were kind and understanding.
3. Both boys had pet dogs.

4. Both Shan and Eli lived in the same part of the country.
5. Both boys lived at about the same time.
6. Both boys had younger brothers.
7. Both boys loved the out-of-doors.
8. Both boys offered to make up for the wrong things that they did.

Discovering New Words

Choose the word from those listed below that best fits in each sentence. If you need help, use your dictionary. Then write the completed sentences in your notebook.

foundation	decision	character
discovered	principle	phlox
customers	alder	fetched

1. Shan made an unwise _____.
2. Shan's mother was anxious for him to be a boy of good _____.
3. The turtle that had come to lay her eggs that morning was somewhere under the cool shade of the _____.

4. Mr. Conley said to Shan, "I see you _____ a basket."
5. Shan's mother said, "One penny or a hundred pennies, Shan, the _____ is the same."
6. "This is a lesson in honesty you won't forget. It gives you a good _____ from your fingertips to your toes!"
7. Wild _____ couldn't grow on the side the tree was, for the tree's giant roots grew above the water.
8. Shan _____ a small hole in the sand.
9. And he had to tell him about the sack with the hole in it. Shan dreaded to do that, too. He hoped there wouldn't be any _____ to hear him.

More Books to Read

BULLA, CLYDE ROBERT. *Indian Hill.*
New York: Thomas Y. Crowell Company, 1963.
   Kee, an Indian boy, moves with his family from their home on the reservation to the city. Kee doesn't like the city, but a visit back home shows him how unfair and narrow-minded he has been.

COATSWORTH, ELIZABETH. *Jon the Unlucky*.

New York: Holt, Rinehart and Winston, 1964.

An orphaned boy, lost in a snowstorm, finds a hidden valley in the wastelands of Greenland. The story is based on historical fact.

ROUNDS, GLEN. *The Blind Colt*.

New York: Holiday House, 1941, 1960.

In this satisfying "Western" a boy keeps a blind colt from being shot. It survives a hard winter and finds security with the boy's help.

STONG, PHIL. *Honk, the Moose*.

New York: Dodd, Mead & Company, 1935.

When Honk the Moose comes to stay in Mr. Ketonen's barn for the winter, no one knows what to do. How do you get rid of a moose that eats as much as four horses and refuses to go back to the woods? Read the story to find out.

STUART, JESSE. *The Beatinest Boy*.

New York: McGraw-Hill Book Company, 1953.

David and Grandma Beverley live in a little Kentucky mountain cabin. At Christmastime, David wants very much to buy a present for his grandmother. But he has no money. So he gives her an unusual gift that only a very smart little boy would have thought of.

Edith Fisher Hunter grew up in New England. As a child she loved school, and in college she studied to become a doctor. Later she decided to be a college teacher, but after her marriage Mrs. Hunter found that all of her teaching was done at home to her own children.

Child of the Silent Night is Mrs. Hunter's first book written especially for children. When she was a little girl, her mother had told her the story of Laura Bridgman. So when Mrs. Hunter's own children heard the story and also became interested, she decided to write a book about Laura and the amazing ways in which she learned to do the things that seeing children can do.

Child of the Silent Night

The Story of Laura Bridgman

EDITH FISHER HUNTER

Illustrated by Bea Holmes

Can you imagine what the world would
be like if you could not see or hear?
How could you learn about things
around you, or how to read or even
to think? This book is the true
story of Laura Bridgman, the first
blind and deaf child ever to be taught
these things. Nearly fifty years later
Helen Keller benefited by the teaching
and experiences that Laura had had.

You will notice throughout this book
that Laura is pictured with a band
across her eyes. The artist has
done this because it was a common
practice at the time Laura lived to
cover the eyes of blind persons.

After you have finished the book,
decide whether you think *Child of
the Silent Night* is a good title for it.

Child of the Silent Night

by Edith Fisher Hunter

Illustrated by Bea Holmes

HOUGHTON MIFFLIN COMPANY   BOSTON
The Riverside Press   Cambridge

Contents

To
Frances Way Fisher
who first introduced me to
the story of
Laura Bridgman

A Room Without Windows or Doors | 1

A little girl was sitting on a granite rock that extended out over a rushing brook. Her legs dangled down near the water, and in her hand she held a long stick. The other end of the stick was deep in the water.

The little girl's name was Laura. On this warm day in early May the brook was so swelled with melted snow that it was almost a river. The swirling water seemed to be trying to pull the stick right out of Laura's hand. She clutched it with all her might. She was not going to let go of it. She would let the brook pull her in before she would let go!

Beside Laura sat Uncle Asa Tenney. He had tight hold of her arm. He knew that although Laura was seven years old, she was not as strong as most seven-year-olds. She certainly was not as strong as a swollen stream in early May in New Hampshire. He had no intention of letting Laura follow her stick into the water.

Laura was wondering as she and Uncle Asa sat there by the brook. She could remember the last time they had taken the walk that brought them here. It had been an icy cold day. There had been some snow still on the ground, and they had worn boots and warm coats. Most amazing of all, they had been able to walk on the brook!

Laura wondered how that could possibly be. How could people walk on brooks when it was very cold, but when it was warm they must be careful not to fall into them? In cold weather, she wondered to herself, does the brook have a cover like the well at home?

Her mother and father never let her go near the well unless the cover was on. But the cover of the well was not slippery like the cover of the brook. She remembered sliding on the brook with Uncle Asa. She would have to think some more about all this.

At last Laura took her stick out of the brook. She was satisfied that she had won the tug-of-war.

She laid the stick on the rock beside her, and felt about until she found a stone to throw into the water. The stone felt smooth. She rubbed it against her cheek.

Oh, she thought, it is a lovely one! I'm not going to throw that one away. She slipped it into her dress pocket to take home. She would put it with the other treasures gathered in her walks with Uncle Asa.

Laura began to feel around for a stone that was not so nice to throw in the brook. This time she found a rough piece of granite and threw it in the direction in which she knew the water lay. Then she wondered whether it really had hit the water. She found a large rock and let it drop directly below her. Laura smiled as the cold water splashed up on her legs. She knew that one had surely hit the water!

Now Uncle Asa pulled on Laura's arm. She knew that meant that it was time to start for home. She had already noticed that the sun did not feel as warm as it had earlier in the afternoon. Probably it was nearing suppertime. Uncle Asa helped her up off the warm rock on which they had been sitting.

As they followed the narrow path that the cows had made from the brook over to the wagon road,

Uncle Asa led the way. He held back the long blackberry brambles and guided Laura carefully. He had to guide Laura because she was blind. She had been blind ever since she was two years old. At that time she had nearly died of scarlet fever.

Laura and Uncle Asa did not say anything as they walked along. If Uncle Asa had said anything, Laura could not have heard him because she was completely deaf. The fever had made her deaf as well as blind.

And Laura did not say anything to Uncle Asa either, because she could not talk. A person who cannot talk is called mute. At the time when Laura lived, children who became deaf before they had learned to talk always became mute. They never learned to speak.

This little girl who could not see or hear or talk was named Laura Bridgman. She was a real little girl and she lived almost 150 years ago in Mill Village, a part of Hanover, New Hampshire. She was born on December 21, 1829. Although as a tiny baby she was not very strong, still she had been able to see and hear. By the time she was two years old she was beginning to say a few words, just as most children do.

And then the dreadful sickness had come. For several months after the fever Laura had lain in a large old cradle in a darkened room. Gradually her father and mother discovered that the sickness had made her blind and deaf. For weeks she could only drink liquids and could not even sit up. It was a whole year before she could walk by herself again, and it was not until she was about five years old that she was nearly as strong as most children her age.

Perhaps she would never have become very healthy if it had not been for her friend Mr. Asa Tenney. The Bridgman family called him Uncle Asa, but he was not a real uncle to them. Most people thought that Asa Tenney was a little queer. Although he seemed very old, he wasn't, really. But his clothes were. He didn't care about things like clothes. All he cared about were out-of-door things —like birds and flowers and brooks, and the little dumb animals that he found on his walks.

And now he had come to care about Laura Bridgman, too. In a way she seemed almost like one of the little helpless creatures of the woods. Like them, she could not tell people what she was thinking and what she wanted. But he knew that she wanted kindness and attention and love.

Mr. Tenney had no family of his own. When he discovered this little girl at neighbor Bridgman's house, he felt that at last he had found someone who needed him.

Daniel and Harmony Bridgman, Laura's father and mother, were kindly people and wanted to do what they could for this poor child of theirs. But they had little time to give her. Mr. Bridgman was a busy farmer and a selectman of the town of Hanover. Mrs. Bridgman had two little boys younger than Laura to care for. In addition, she had to do all the things that any farm wife did in those days.

She had a flock of sheep that must be tended. Their wool had to be spun and made into cloth. She also spun and wove flax. This cloth and the woolen cloth had to be made into clothes for her family. Mrs. Bridgman also kept bees and chickens. She made soap and candles and all of her own bread. And, of course, there were all the meals to get and all the washing and ironing to do.

In most farm homes a large family was a fine thing to have because the children could begin to help at an early age. But Laura's two older sisters had died from scarlet fever at the time Laura was sick. Now there were no older children to help.

334

No, Mrs. Bridgman did not have much time to teach her little deaf, blind, mute daughter. Even if there had been time, how could she have taught Laura anything? Can a person who cannot see or hear or talk learn anything?

Asa Tenney was sure Laura could learn. He believed that she was learning every minute and that she wanted to learn a great deal more. He knew that he had plenty of time in which to teach her, too.

He explained it to himself this way: "It is as though Laura is living in a room without windows or doors. I must make windows and doors into that room."

Uncle Asa and the Stranger | 2

Just as soon as Laura was well enough to be out of doors much, Uncle Asa had begun taking her on excursions. At first they were short ones, just around the farm itself. On these first walks he carried Laura a good part of the time. But as she grew stronger, the two friends were able to go farther and farther in their explorations.

Uncle Asa knew that he could not tell Laura what they were seeing or where they were going, and so he let the world itself do the telling. That is why, when they visited the brook in winter, he let Laura walk on the ice and feel it hard and cold under her feet. And that is why, when they were at the brook this day, he found a long stick and let her feel the wildly rushing water pull it.

Now, as they walked toward the Bridgman farm late on this lovely May day, Uncle Asa saw another way in which the world itself could tell Laura that spring had come to New Hampshire.

A big mother robin was sitting high on an apple tree in the orchard at the side of the road. She was shouting out her "cheerio, cheer-up, cheerily" just as loudly as possible. A fat father robin was standing in the road ahead. He was tugging a plump worm out of a wet wagon rut. There, now he had him, and father robin flew straight to the tree where mother robin was singing. He disappeared below her among the blossom-covered branches.

Of course Laura could not see or hear any of these things. But Uncle Asa had carefully noticed just exactly where the father bird disappeared among the branches. He touched Laura's arm. She understood what he meant by that touch. She was to stand perfectly still and wait right where she was at the side of the road until he came back.

He started over into the orchard. Quickly he climbed into the low crotch of the tree on which the mother robin was singing. The singing stopped. Uncle Asa went on climbing until he came to the branch where he thought the father robin had gone in. As he brushed back the branches, there was a quick flutter of wings and the father robin flew out. Then as Uncle Asa leaned on the branch, he was greeted with a loud chorus of peeps.

"Ho, ho! Just as I thought—a family of baby robins. Yes, there's the nest, and, let me see—one, two, three, four babies."

The baby birds seemed to be about two weeks old. They were not all naked as newly hatched birds are, but had plenty of feathers. Their eyes were open, and so were their mouths!

"Peep, peep, peep, peep," they shouted, their long skinny necks stretched tall and their mouths wide open. They thought Uncle Asa was their mother or father bringing them worms. Each one wanted to be sure to get a good big mouthful!

"Sorry, little birds," said Uncle Asa, "I don't have anything for you. I just wanted to know exactly where you were. I want my little friend Laura to meet one of you. We won't hurt you. I'm sure if you could understand all about Laura, you wouldn't mind a bit. I'll be back in a minute."

Uncle Asa climbed down the tree and walked over to the wagon road where Laura stood waiting. He took her hand and led her into the orchard. He helped her find a comfortable place to sit, in the grass by the trunk of the tree.

The mother and father robin were both quite upset by the return of this visitor to their nursery. They were far up in the branches of the tree making the worried cry that robins make at such times. They kept up their troubled calling as Uncle Asa climbed up again to the branch that held their nest.

Very carefully and gently he lifted out one baby robin. "Peep, peep, peep," it cried. Never before had it felt a person's hand, and it didn't think it liked it one bit.

"Don't you worry, little bird; I'll put you back in just a few minutes," and Uncle Asa climbed down the tree with the frightened bird cuddled close to him.

With his free hand he arranged Laura's hands in the shape of a cup. Then he put the live ball of feathers in the nest made of hands.

A smile spread across Laura's face. She had learned to expect surprises like this on her walks with Uncle Asa. She felt the warm bird, so soft and frightened. Of course she could not hear the peeping noises it was making, but she could feel the quick beating of its heart and the wild flapping of its tiny wings.

Little by little Laura had learned that with small, soft, breathing things she must be very, very careful. Once, when she was younger, Uncle Asa had brought a tiny animal to her to hold. It was a baby rabbit. She had been so excited that she had grabbed it tightly around the neck, and before Uncle Asa could rescue it, she had stopped its breathing. Now Laura knew that if she were gentle with such things, they would go on breathing and feeling warm.

Sometimes Uncle Asa caught funny slippery creatures down by the brook. They were not warm, but they wiggled and kicked. Laura had learned to hold frogs tightly enough so that they could not jump out of her hands and yet not so tightly that they could never jump out again.

Of course Laura did not know the names we use for any of these things—birds or rabbits or frogs. She just knew the things themselves.

The little bird in Laura's hands did not seem so frightened now. It was still crouched down and

breathing heavily, but it was not flapping its wings.
Laura could feel the bird's claws curled around
her fingers. She felt the little beak peck at her
hands, but she was not afraid. She even put her
cheek close to the soft back for a moment to feel
the downy feathers against her skin. Laura could
feel softness just as well as you or I can.

Uncle Asa could hear the mother and father robin
still uttering their worried cries in the tree above.

He decided that it was time to return the baby bird to its nest. Taking the bird from Laura, he climbed up the tree once more and put it back with the others.

"Thank you, little bird. I'm sure Laura loved holding you even though you may not have loved being held. Laura and I will go right home now, and your mother and father can come and feed you."

Back to the wagon road walked the two friends and up the hill toward the Bridgman farm. The sun was really low now, and the sky was layered with pink and red and gray. Laura could not see how beautiful it was, and there was no way that Uncle Asa could show that beauty to her.

Now he could see the smoke rising from the Bridgman chimney. Another turn of the road brought them within sight of the house itself. Uncle Asa stopped short. That stranger's horse was tied outside the Bridgman farm again!

Laura could tell that something was troubling her good friend. She waited patiently until he was ready to start on. She could not hear him muttering crossly to himself, "I don't like him. Why is he always watching Laura? I wish he'd go away and stay away!"

When they arrived at the door of the house, Uncle Asa knocked heavily before opening the door and going in.

"I thought that must be you and Laura," said Mrs. Bridgman, looking up. "You must be tired and hungry, Asa. Won't you stay and have supper with us tonight? Mr. Barrett will be with us again, and one more guest is no trouble."

"No, thank you, Mrs. Bridgman," said Uncle Asa. "I must be getting right home. I have my chores to do, and I'll want to turn in early."

As he started to go, a young man came across the room. "Good evening, Mr. Tenney. I do wish you would accept Mrs. Bridgman's invitation. You could tell us all about what you and Laura have been doing. Her cheeks are so rosy that I'm sure she has had a wonderful time."

"No, I must go," said Uncle Asa, rather gruffly.

"Well, I'm sure that if Laura could thank you she would," said the young man. "She is a lucky little girl to have such a wonderful friend."

"Hmph!" said Uncle Asa. "Who wants thanks? I don't. Laura's company is the only thanks I want. But I do want that!" And he hurried out the door toward home.

As soon as Laura came into the big farm kitchen, she found her little rocking chair and settled herself in it. The chair was in its usual place, drawn up at one side of the huge fireplace.

The air had grown chill toward the end of the afternoon, and now the fire felt good to Laura. This fire had to be kept going almost all the time, even in warm weather. It was not only the family furnace but also the family cookstove. Mrs. Bridgman did her cooking either in the hot coals or on kettles hung from the crane or in the big oven in the back of the fireplace.

She was busy cooking supper now, stirring something in one large kettle, looking quickly into another. As Laura sat rocking, she could not smell the good smells that filled the kitchen. Her sense of smell had also been almost completely destroyed by the fever that made her deaf and blind. But she could feel the warmth of the fire, and she could feel the comfortable rhythm of her own rocking.

In another minute she could feel something else, too. Patches, the family cat, hopped up into her lap. There was no place that Patches liked better for her long snoozes than Laura's lap. And Laura loved to have the big family pet take her naps there. She could not see the different-colored patches of fur that gave the cat her name, but she could feel the deep softness of the fur. And although Laura could not hear the steady purring of the contented cat, she could feel it through the fur.

Thanks to her walks with Uncle Asa, Laura knew more about living things now. She knew that cats like to sit beside the fire but not *in* the fire. Once, when she was much younger, she had thrown the family cat, Blackie, right into the fire. The poor creature had been badly burned before Mrs. Bridgman was able to rescue it, and then it had run away and never come back. Laura would never again do such a thing to something alive. She knew better now. She was glad to have her friend Patches use her lap as a bed.

But now another friend was looking for a bed. Laura's younger brother, Addison, came toddling across the room. "Laura home," he told his mother as he clambered up into Laura's lap. Patches moved over. She was used to sharing her comfortable bed with Addison.

In just a few minutes the warm fire, the regular rocking, and the steady purring of the cat put little brother to sleep. Laura could tell he was asleep even though she could not see his drowsy eyes close. She felt his head drop heavily on her arm and his fat little hand that rested in hers lie still.

In a moment more Laura might have dropped off to sleep, too. But just then her mother came over and took sleepy little brother from her lap. Mrs. Bridgman put him in the large cradle that stood in a corner of the room. This was the cradle in which

Laura had slept as a baby and in which she had lain sick for so many months.

Then Mrs. Bridgman brushed the cat from Laura's lap and placed some spoons in her daughter's hand. Laura knew that her mother was asking her to set the table for supper. She was glad to help

when she could, and setting the table was one thing that she could do easily and well.

She knew that her father's place was at the head of the table. Next to him on one side she very often set an extra place for Uncle Asa or some other guest. If there was to be a guest, her mother gave her the necessary number of extra spoons. Tonight Mr. Barrett would sit in the guest's seat. On the other side of her father Laura set her own place. Laura sat near her father so that he could give her help as she needed it during a meal.

Then Laura set her mother's place at the other end of the table. On either side of her mother she set places for her two little brothers. Laura knew exactly where to find the forks and knives that were needed. She could also find the napkins and plates by herself. She knew that one very dented pewter plate belonged to her four-year-old brother, John, and the other plate that was slightly less dented to her two-year-old brother, Addison.

And of course she knew her own plate. It had been a present from Uncle Asa. There were decorations around the outer edge of the plate— the letters of the alphabet raised up so that Laura could feel them. Often, as she sat silently at the table during a long meal, she traced their outlines with her fingertip. She wondered what the lines were. Would she ever know?

While Laura was setting the table, James Barrett, the young man who was there, watched her. He had come to think that Laura was the most amazing little girl he had ever seen. The more he watched her, the more wonderful he thought she was.

James Barrett was a student at Dartmouth College in Hanover. He was doing part-time work for Mr. Bridgman in order to earn some extra money. A selectman like Mr. Bridgman helps to run the business of a small town. James Barrett had been hired to help with some of the many records that a selectman must keep.

He had noticed Laura on the very first day that he had come from Hanover to work. At first, although he could see that she was not just like other children, he did not know all of the reasons. Gradually he discovered that she was blind, deaf, and mute. When he felt that he knew Mrs. Bridgman well enough, he asked her about Laura, and she told him the whole sad story.

Day after day as he sat working on the town records at a table in the kitchen, he could not help stopping at frequent intervals to watch Laura. The thing that made her seem so remarkable was that she did not just sit in a chair all day, as he rather expected such a child would, but instead moved about the house and farm eager to learn and to know what was going on.

Although she could not hear or see her mother as she busily did her many chores, Laura could feel the floor or even the air vibrate as her mother moved about. Catching hold of her mother's skirts, she would follow her. If Mrs. Bridgman were making bread and kneading the dough, Laura would place her hands on her mother's arms and knead it with her. Sometimes her mother gave her a lump of dough to knead and shape by herself. Often Laura worked along with her mother as she spun, wove cloth on her heavy loom, or did the churning.

As James Barrett watched Laura, he wondered about many things. Perhaps someday he would be a teacher. How would he set about teaching such a child? We learn, he reflected to himself, by thinking, by using our brains. But what makes our brains work? Our eyes send picture messages to our brains, and so we think about what we are seeing. But Laura's eyes don't send any messages to her brain.

Our ears send sound messages to our brains, he thought. But Laura's ears don't send any messages to her brain. Our noses and the taste buds on our tongues send messages about smells and tastes to our brains, but Mrs. Bridgman has told me that Laura can smell and taste almost nothing. She will take the most horrid-tasting and -smelling medicine without showing any signs of having tasted or smelled it.

So what keeps a person like Laura thinking and exploring? pondered young James Barrett. How is the world getting into her mind? Only through her sense of touch. Whatever she can feel with her hands, her feet, or the skin all over her body can get to her brain.

Laura certainly used her hands. They were almost never still. How could she let them rest when they had to do the work of her four useless senses as well as their own work? They had no time to waste. They were constantly reaching out, feeling everything they lighted upon, and feeling for things they had not yet found.

Soon after James Barrett had come to help Mr. Bridgman, Laura had discovered him working at the table by the kitchen window. Immediately she had begun feeling his clothes, his hands, and up toward his face.

Then Laura's father had stamped his foot. Instantly Laura had stopped her explorations. She had learned that when her father stamped like that, it meant she must stop whatever she was doing. If she didn't, her father became very cross. James Barrett wondered how Laura had "heard" her father stamp his foot. Mr. Bridgman explained that she had felt the floor vibrate. She was "hearing" with her feet.

Later that day, when Mr. Bridgman had gone out, James Barrett had let Laura feel his face. "After all," he explained to Mrs. Bridgman, "that is the only way in which Laura can know what I look like. She has to 'see' me through her fingers. Even a child who can really see, if he is allowed, wants to touch things at first so he can know more about them. How much more important it is for little Laura to be able to feel things!"

James Barrett had decided that one reason Laura learned so much in her walks with Asa Tenney was that he let her feel and handle and touch so many different things. He wished that Mr. Tenney would be more friendly toward him. He wanted to talk with him about Laura. He wanted to ask him many questions about his ways of teaching her.

But no! The minute he started to ask him anything about Laura, Mr. Tenney would become cold and unfriendly and start for home. Anyone could see that he loved Laura. Then why didn't he want to talk about her?

Now, as Laura was setting the table, James Barrett spoke to Mrs. Bridgman about this. "It was the same way again tonight, did you notice? The minute I began to show some interest in Laura, Mr. Tenney got almost angry with me. Why? Why should he?"

"I think I know," said Mrs. Bridgman slowly. "Poor Asa has had a lonely life with no family of his own for years. Until he found Laura, he had no one to love and to take care of except the baby birds he found fallen from their nests, or a hurt rabbit, or some other helpless creature. In Laura he has found someone who really needs him. I think he is afraid that somehow he'll lose Laura if you become interested in her."

"Poor old man," said James Barrett. "I don't know why he thinks he might lose Laura because of me. I don't know where he thinks I could take her. There aren't any schools for children like Laura. At least, I don't think there are."

Laura had finished setting the table for her mother, but Mr. Bridgman had not yet come in from the evening chores. Laura went over to one corner of the kitchen where there was an old cabinet.

James Barrett was watching her, and he knew why she went there. That was where she kept her very strange "doll." It was not a real doll, but an old leather boot that she often held in her lap. She seemed to think of it as a doll. She rocked it and cuddled it in much the same way that she held her little brother.

It was this boot that Laura had gone to get. James Barrett watched her. First she found a large key on a shelf near the cabinet. With the key she opened a low door in the cabinet. She had learned that she must keep this door locked if her boot were to be safe from her two little brothers.

Taking her boot, she went over and sat down in her rocking chair. She reached into her skirt pocket and took out the smooth stone that she had found on her afternoon walk. He watched her feel it and brush it against her cheek. Then he saw her take her boot and turn it gently on its side.

Out onto her lap rolled several small objects. James Barrett already knew what they were—treasures found on her walks with Uncle Asa. There were several stones. One was flat and shiny. He watched Laura peel off a thin layer of the stone. No matter how many times she peeled off a layer, there always seemed to be another one. This was mica. He wished Laura could see this amazing "stone."

The next one of her treasures was a bluejay feather. She drew it through her fingers, making all the barbs go in one direction. After a few minutes she laid it down and picked up something that looked like a toothpick. It was round and smooth, white at one end and black at the other. He had asked Mrs. Bridgman what it was one day, and she had said it was a porcupine quill. Laura had let him feel it. It was as soft and smooth as silk until he touched the tip of it. That had a tiny hook on the end. Laura was careful to avoid touching that.

The next treasure that Laura took out was a fat,
bumpy, dull-green thing. Some white fluff was coming out of it. This was a milkweed pod. Laura and
Uncle Asa had found it in the fall. Now it was dry
and brittle on the outside. Laura ran her fingers
over the silky down attached to the seeds. How soft
it was! Some of the seeds had escaped and lay
loose among the treasures on her lap. She carefully
tucked them back into the pod. In the fall, when
she and Uncle Asa were walking in the fields, they

359

had found lots of these pods. Sometimes he made her blow at them. Laura wondered why.

Now James Barrett watched as Laura took out a small object and ran her finger around and around on it. That must be the empty snail shell they had found last week. He had watched Laura and Uncle Asa as they sat on the granite doorstep by the kitchen. Uncle Asa had held Laura's hand and helped her trace the spiral shape of the shell with one finger. James Barrett wondered what her brain could think as her fingers traced the spiral pattern. What is a spiral to a mind that has never seen one?

Finally Laura reached into the toe of the boot and brought out a tiny box. She took out a large section of a broken robin's egg. Some mother robin had thrown it out of the nest after a baby robin had pecked its way out. Mother robins are good house-keepers! Laura could not see the lovely blue coloring of the shell, but she could feel its smoothness.

Suddenly Laura stopped feeling her treasures and looked up. She was listening and hearing something, not with her ears, but with her whole body. She knew that the door of the farm kitchen had opened and then closed. Probably it was her father coming in. Laura went back to her treasures.

But so did someone else! Brother John had come up beside Laura and had taken one of her treasures. Too late, Laura felt his hand in her lap. Quick as lightning she reached out for his hand, but he was even quicker. Laura felt wildly about in the air. There! She had him by the arm. She gripped him as tightly as she could.

Brother John began to bellow. Of course, Laura could not hear him. Frightened, he dropped the shell and in a moment more had stepped on it. Laura was shaking him with the hand that gripped him and feeling about for her treasures with the other hand. John went on screaming.

Suddenly Laura stopped shaking him, although she did not loosen her hold. She had felt her father stamp his foot. There, he stamped it again. She knew that she should let go of her brother. But he had taken one of her treasures. She was sure he had. No! She would not let go of him, not until he gave it back. They were hers! She hung on to him. She began shaking him again.

A moment later Laura felt her father's powerful hand take hold of her. She felt a blow on her hand that was clutching her brother, and she let go. But now she was like a furious wild animal. All of her treasures were being scattered on the floor. She began crying and making the strange, unpleasant sound that she could and did make when upset. Again Laura felt a blow from her father's powerful hand, and she fell in a limp ball on the floor, sobbing.

Laura could not hear her father apologizing to James Barrett for the dreadful behavior of his daughter. "I don't know what we can do," said Mr. Bridgman. "She always used to obey me the moment I stamped my foot, but now she has become more willful. I do not like to strike her, but scenes such as this have occurred more and more of late."

James Barrett was listening respectfully to Mr. Bridgman's apology. But he was also looking for Laura's scattered treasures. Fearful that Mr. Bridgman might take offense, nonetheless he tried to defend Laura.

"I saw it all happen, sir. She was playing with her treasures when John crept up and snatched one from her lap. Had I been quicker, I might have stopped him. Don't be too harsh with the child. She is a truly wonderful little girl."

In silence Mr. Bridgman turned away to prepare himself for supper. James Barrett searched the floor and found the stones, the milkweed pod, the feather, and in between the wide boards of the floor the porcupine quill. Alas, the robin's egg shell and the snail shell lay crushed. He found Laura's boot and helped her place the stones, seed pod, feather, and quill back inside, but he could not make her understand what had happened to the shells.

The boot was placed back on the shelf and the cupboard locked with the big key. The family and guest gathered around the supper table.

"I fear," said Mr. Bridgman, "that Laura will become more and more like a wild animal. She was the smartest of any of our children before this dreadful affliction came upon her. Now, I am afraid, she cannot be taught anything."

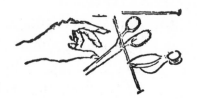

As he rode his horse back to college that evening, James Barrett could think of nothing but Laura Bridgman. He did not hear the robins singing their late "cheerio-cheer-up's." He did not see the apple blossoms that covered the orchard trees so that there seemed to be great vases of flowers along the road. He did not smell the blossom-laden lilac bushes that stood by the farmhouse doors as he rode past. For the time being it was almost as if he, too, were deaf and blind and dull of senses, his thoughts were so busy with Laura Bridgman.

Of course she is becoming more and more dis-obedient! thought James Barrett to himself. She is so bright and so interested in things that she cannot be easily held back. She knew that those were her very own treasures and that little John would spoil them. She disobeyed her father because she cared so much about them. If only she could tell people what she wants and why she does things. But she can't! She probably never can!

Even a night's sleep did not entirely clear James Barrett's mind of such thoughts. He went to his first class at college in the morning only half prepared in his lessons and not able to concentrate on what the teacher was saying. The class was one in anatomy, the study of the human body, and the teacher was Dr. Reuben Mussey. Dr. Mussey was one of James Barrett's favorite teachers, and it suddenly occurred to James that Dr. Mussey might be interested in hearing about Laura.

After the class was over, he told Dr. Mussey all about Laura Bridgman. He was glad to be able to share his enthusiasm and concern for this remarkable little girl with someone outside the family.

"I just wish that you would come out to the Bridgman farm with me sometime, sir, and see her for yourself. It is just amazing to me that she knows as much as she does."

"Well, James," said Dr. Mussey, "I would indeed be very much interested in seeing this child. You know how much I feel we have still to discover about the human body and mind, and how they work. But do you think that the Bridgmans would welcome my coming? They might think I was just curious."

"I believe that Mr. Bridgman would be most happy to have you come, especially if he thought that you might be able to help in some way. After all, he knows how difficult it is to make Laura obey him now. He knows he needs help."

"I wish that I thought I really could be of some assistance," said Dr. Mussey, "but I doubt that there is anything much that can be done for such a child. Your enthusiasm makes me want to see her, however, if you are sure that no one will mind my coming."

"Well," said James Barrett, "I can't truthfully say that *no one* will mind. Mr. and Mrs. Bridgman won't, I'm sure, but Mr. Tenney will probably mind a good deal." And James Barrett told Dr. Mussey all about Laura's wonderful but suspicious friend.

Professor Mussey was very much interested in what James Barrett told him about Mr. Tenney. "He must be a remarkable teacher. I would like to see him and Laura together. He has probably found many ways to communicate with her other than through words. See if you can arrange a visit to the Bridgmans' at a time when Mr. Tenney will be there also."

The next week, on Thursday, Dr. Mussey and James Barrett drove together to the Bridgman farm. They arrived in the early afternoon, having been invited to remain for supper also.

Mrs. Bridgman told them that Laura and Uncle Asa were out in the back meadow feeding the sheep. They walked around behind the big barn and looked across to the meadow. A flock of sheep was grazing there.

"I don't want Mr. Tenney to think that we are spying on him," said James Barrett, "but I'm afraid that if he sees us right away, he'll just bring Laura back to the house and go home. There they are; do you see them?"

"Yes, I see them," said Dr. Mussey. "Let's start over in their direction. Both of them have their backs to us and seem very busy with something. Perhaps they won't notice us for a bit."

As they came closer, they could see that Uncle Asa had brought a pewter bottle of milk. He was taking it out of his jacket pocket. They watched as he gave it to Laura. She sat right down in the grass with it, and a young, still wobbly-legged little lamb came running over to her. The lamb went down on its knees in front of her. Laura popped the bottle of milk into its mouth.

"Even a child who can see and hear couldn't have more fun than that," said Dr. Mussey. "They must have done this many times before. Laura knew just what to do. Let's go over there, James. I want to meet Mr. Tenney. Surely he won't go off and leave Laura feeding the lamb alone."

James Barrett was not at all sure that Asa Tenney would not leave when *he* came into sight, but he took Dr. Mussey over anyway. Laura, busy with the lamb, did not notice their arrival in any way.

"Mr. Tenney," said James Barrett, "I would like to introduce Dr. Mussey. He is one of my teachers at the College. I have told him a great deal about you and Laura."

Uncle Asa did not look at all pleased at the arrival of a second stranger who was interested in Laura. It was bad enough having James Barrett watching Laura so much, and now he was bringing his friends to see her, too!

"How do you do," he said quite gruffly. "Laura's busy feeding an orphan lamb, as you can see."

Dr. Mussey shook hands with Mr. Tenney, and then he asked, "Why doesn't one of the other mother sheep feed this baby?"

"Sheep are funny that way," said Uncle Asa, forgetting to be unfriendly. "They don't like to adopt another ewe's baby, even if it is motherless."

"I didn't realize that," said Dr. Mussey. "What kind of sheep are these?"

Uncle Asa's face began to brighten. This stranger seemed much more interested in farm animals than in Laura. After Laura had finished feeding the lamb, they went to the barn to gather eggs. Dr. Mussey wanted to know just what kind of hens they were and how many eggs they usually laid each day. When they visited the pigs, he wanted to know what the pigs had been fed to make them so fat so early in the year.

In a very short time Dr. Mussey and Asa Tenney were the best of friends. James Barrett went back to the farmhouse to do some of his regular work on Mr. Bridgman's papers. Uncle Asa and Laura and Dr. Mussey finished the chores, explored the woods at the edge of the meadow, and just generally had a fine time.

Dr. Mussey didn't ask a single question about Laura. But that didn't mean that he wasn't interested in her or that he wasn't finding out a great deal. But he knew something that young James Barrett did not know.

He knew that if he seemed to show no interest in Laura, Mr. Tenney would not feel frightened and uneasy. At the same time, because Laura was right there with them, Uncle Asa couldn't help showing Dr. Mussey some of his ways of teaching her.

Dr. Mussey was also able to see that Laura and Uncle Asa had a kind of sign language that they used with each other. For example, a slight push meant that they were going somewhere, a pull meant that she wanted to show him something. If she raised her hand to her lips, it meant that she wanted a drink from the well. If she sat down as they were walking, it meant that she was tired and wanted to rest. There were many other signs that passed between Uncle Asa and Laura that a person less interested than Dr. Mussey might not have noticed.

One thing was very clear to him—Laura was indeed a very bright little girl, and she could use her mind wonderfully well in spite of being deaf, blind, mute, and almost without a sense of taste or smell. Before they sat down to supper, Dr. Mussey was able to carry out a few simple tests on Laura about which he wrote a report sometime later. At the end of this report he said: "She was considered by her parents as unusually intelligent before her sickness, and is still so regarded by them."

In a short time Mrs. Bridgman called her family and the three guests to supper. Mr. Tenney, Dr.

Mussey, and Mr. Bridgman were soon busily engaged in conversation. James Barrett had been careful to take a place next to Laura. As the others were talking, James took Laura's little hand and guided it over to something beside his plate.

Laura's face brightened. James Barrett was helping her trace the spiral shape on a new snail shell; one of her lost treasures had mysteriously returned! Then he placed something close to her other hand —the smooth, rounded end of a large section of a robin's egg! Again a smile spread over Laura's face; her second lost treasure was found.

Little did Laura know how many hours James Barrett had spent, when he should have been studying, looking under damp rocks for an empty snail shell and under apple trees for a section of an eggshell, thrown from the nest by some busy mother robin. When the meal was over, he helped Laura put her treasures safely away in her boot.

As Dr. Mussey and James Barrett rode back through the lush green New Hampshire countryside, Dr. Mussey said, "I have a plan, James; let's see what comes of it."

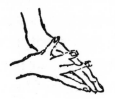

Young Dr. Samuel Gridley Howe was sitting reading by a window in his apartment. For five years he had been the director of the first school for the blind in the United States. This school in Boston, Massachusetts, was called the New England Asylum for the Blind. It had been founded in 1829 by Dr. John D. Fisher. In 1832 Dr. Howe had been appointed the first director.

In five years he had seen the school grow from a few rooms in his own father's home with just a handful of pupils to a real school housed in a beautiful mansion, a gift from wealthy Colonel Thomas Perkins. Later, when the school was moved to even larger quarters in South Boston, it was renamed Perkins Institution. Moved again, in

1912, to Watertown, Massachusetts, it is now known all over the world as Perkins School for the Blind.

At this time Dr. Howe was not married and lived with his unmarried sister, Miss Jeannette Howe, in a small apartment in the school. Miss Jeannette, as everyone called her, was busy sewing as Dr. Howe sat reading by the window. The cool June breeze felt refreshing to the tired young director who took his job so seriously.

Suddenly he became very excited about something he was reading. "By Jove!" he said aloud. "She sounds like just the child I have been hoping to find."

"Who does?" asked Miss Jeannette, looking up from her sewing. "What child have you been hoping to find."

"There is a report here," said the young doctor, "written by my friend Dr. Reuben Mussey of Dartmouth College. It tells of a remarkable child who has recently been brought to his attention. She lives on a farm in the outskirts of Hanover. The child has been deaf, blind, mute, and practically without a sense of taste or smell since the age of two. He reports quite fully about his visit to observe her in her home and says that in spite of these many handicaps she is an unusually alert and clever child."

"What is her name?" asked Miss Jeannette.

"Her name is Laura Bridgman. She is seven years old and in good health. She does simple household tasks as well as chores about the farm. She even sews and knits with some skill. But most important of all, he says she is as eager to learn and as curious about all that goes on around her as any normal seven-year-old. He wonders if perhaps she could not be educated.

"Jeannette, you know how eager I have been to find a child like this and to experiment with some of my ideas about the education of the deaf-blind. I am sure that she is the one I should begin with."

"But, Sam," said Miss Jeannette, "don't you have enough to do now without attempting such a hopeless task? You know how unsuccessful they have been in the attempt to educate Julia Brace down in Hartford. She, too, is deaf, blind, and mute. She just doesn't seem to want to learn."

"That is just the point," said Dr. Howe. "This child *is* eager to learn, according to Dr. Mussey's report. Her own curiosity and eagerness will be as important as anything I will be able to do. Don't forget, Julia Brace was nearly thirty years old when they attempted to educate her. Seven is a golden age for learning. I am determined to go to Hanover and see this child myself. If Dr. Mussey is right about her ability, and I know what a careful observer he is, I intend to seek her parents' permission to bring her here to the school in the fall."

"Well, I only hope that you are not going to be disappointed, Sam," said Miss Jeannette.

"I feel sure that I won't be," said Dr. Howe enthusiastically. "I'll write Dr. Mussey tonight and ask him to make arrangements for me to visit the little girl in July. Our school will be having vacation. I had thought of going to the graduation at Dartmouth then, anyhow."

It was an excited Dr. Mussey who, a few days later, reported to an equally excited James Barrett the arrival of a letter from the distinguished Dr. Samuel Gridley Howe.

"He says," Dr. Mussey explained, "that there has never been a child as handicapped as Laura educated at his school. He says that, to his knowledge, no deaf, blind, and mute person has ever been successfully educated anywhere. But he has been eager to try to educate just such a child. I think our Laura is going to have her chance."

The very next day Dr. Mussey made a visit to the Bridgman farm and received permission to bring Dr. Howe to see Laura in July. He explained that Dr. Howe was hopeful about the possibility of educating her at his school.

Mr. and Mrs. Bridgman were most grateful to Dr. Mussey. They were realizing more acutely each day that unless something were done soon for their intelligent little daughter, she would become wholly unmanageable.

But Dr. Mussey could not convince Asa Tenney that any good would come from Dr. Howe's visit. Uncle Asa was certain that he himself could teach Laura all she would ever need to know.

"Haven't I taught her to love the creatures of the woods and the flowers of the fields?" he asked Dr. Mussey. "She has waded in the brook in summer, slid on the ice in winter, and felt its power when it is swollen in the spring. She has raised lambs, learned to find the hidden nests of hens, and held newborn kittens and puppies in her hands.

"I have taught her in the only way that she can learn—through her hands. What can they teach her in a school? Teachers whom she cannot hear using books that she cannot see! The great out-of-doors is the best schoolroom there is for any child, but even more so for Laura."

"Yes, Asa," said Dr. Mussey, "what you have done for Laura is wonderful. Without your teaching no other teacher would be able to do anything. You have kept alive her curiosity and eagerness to learn. You have given her wonderful experiences. But you yourself have seen what is happening more and more often now. She flies into a rage and is almost like a caged animal when she wants something but cannot make those around her understand *what* she wants."

Asa Tenney looked uncomfortably down at the ground. He knew exactly what Dr. Mussey meant. Just a few days before, he and Laura had gone out to salt the sheep. Laura had wanted to feed the baby lamb a bottle of milk again. Uncle Asa had no way of telling her that the lamb had now grown too big and could feed itself. Determined little Laura had searched in every one of Uncle Asa's pockets for the bottle of milk and, furious at not finding it, had reached up and caught hold of his glasses. She had torn them off his face and crushed them on the ground.

"You do not want Mr. Bridgman to have to treat her like a dumb animal, whipping her if she will not obey him," said Dr. Mussey gently. "Dr. Howe believes that Laura can be taught to understand our words and to talk with us. Surely you, who have set her free this far, won't stand in the way of giving her even greater freedom?"

"Oh, I have nothing to say about it," said Asa Tenney in despair. "If Mr. Bridgman thinks that this Dr. Howe can make a blind child see, a deaf child hear, and a mute child talk, who am I to contradict him?"

"He, too, will have to work through Laura's hands, Asa, just as you have," said Dr. Mussey. "Those wonderful hands that you have helped to make so sensitive."

But nothing that was said could convince Asa Tenney that sending Laura to school in Boston was going to be a good thing. And nothing would induce him to be on hand on the afternoon when the carriage with Dr. Mussey and Dr. Howe arrived at the Bridgman farm.

Laura never forgot her first meeting with Dr. Samuel Gridley Howe. He was an unusually tall man, and she was just a little girl. His great height combined with his great gentleness made a lasting impression.

When he took her small hand in his large one on that July afternoon in New Hampshire, there began an adventure in education that was to become famous all over the United States and parts of Europe.

Even in the short visit that he made that day Dr. Howe caught a glimpse of Laura Bridgman's unusual quickness and intelligence. Like James Barrett and Dr. Mussey before him, he was much impressed, and knew that Laura Bridgman was the child with whom to carry on his first experiment in the education of the deaf-blind.

As a result of the visit it was agreed that Laura would go to Dr. Howe's school in the fall.

It was Columbus Day, October 12, 1837, just a few weeks before her eighth birthday, when Laura Bridgman started out on her great adventure. Seated in a light carriage, called a chaise, between her father and mother, Laura was tense with excitement. Where was she going? No one could tell her.

Why had she helped her mother put the best of her old clothes and many new ones in a large trunk that she knew was in the carriage with them? Why had her treasures been taken out of her boot and put in a box in among her clothes?

Laura knew that something very unusual was happening. Exactly what it was she did not know, but at least her parents were with her.

Of course she could not see how beautiful Hanover was on this October day. As yet there had been no killing frost, and the late autumn flowers, especially the goldenrod and asters, were lovely. The sugar maples were at the peak of their golden glory, and the red maples were brilliant to the seeing eye. The woodbine curled like tongues of fire up and around the trees along the road. Laura did not know that she was saying good-by to all this beauty for a while.

But there was someone who did know. From a rise of ground in the back meadow Asa Tenney watched the chaise drive away from the Bridgman farm. There were tears in his eyes. How right he had been to think that no good could come from the visits of that first stranger, James Barrett. No good had come! Laura was being taken away from him. His worst fears had come true.

This October there would be no one to take tramping through the piles of fallen maple leaves. There would be no one for whom to gather fat milkweed pods. And why should he bother this year to find the plumpest apples in the orchard or the fallen hickory nuts along the stone wall?

Laura was gone. The light had gone out of Asa Tenney's life. It was never to be lighted quite so brightly again. Although Laura did visit home and Uncle Asa saw her many times, it was never the same again for him.

But a light was soon to be lighted in the life of Laura Bridgman that was to shine into the lives of deaf-blind children all over the world. And because of the hours he had spent taking a little deaf-blind child to the meadows and woods, the name of Asa Tenney has not been forgotten.

The trip from Hanover to Boston was a long one in those days. The Bridgmans had to change from the chaise to a stagecoach and spend several days along the way. Never had Laura been on such a long journey; never had she felt herself in the midst of so many strangers. She tried to hide behind her mother's skirts and her father's great-coat. When would they get to wherever it was they were going?

After what must have seemed to Laura an endlessly long time the coach finally stopped. Mr. and Mrs. Bridgman and Laura were helped out. Laura clung to her mother as they went up a short flight of stairs and into a building. In another moment Laura felt her small hand once again held by the large hand that belonged to the unusually tall man who had visited her once in Mill Village. Was this

his home? What was she doing here? No one could explain, of course.

Then Laura felt a woman's soft hand take hers. Laura could not know that this was Miss Jeannette Howe. Laura and her mother took off their coats and bonnets. Following the strange woman, they walked along—what was it? A room? A hall? Laura could somehow sense the largeness of the rooms. She was accustomed to small, low-ceilinged rooms at home. She felt very small and lost in so much space. She clung to the strange but friendly woman on one side of her and to her mother on the other.

Now they had entered a smaller room, and she was allowed to feel about. There was a bed, a rocking chair, a washstand, and a little table. The furnishings here were not unlike those in her own room at the farm. She was encouraged to help her mother take her dresses and other clothes out of the trunk in which they had been placed at home. Were they perhaps going to stay here for a visit? Where was her mother's bag?

There, now they had come to her box of treasures. She felt her mother take it and place it on the table by the bed. Was this going to be her own room? Would her little brothers, Addison and John, be coming, too? Would her treasures be safe on the table? No one can know whether questions such as these passed through Laura's mind, and no one, of course, could have made her understand the answers to them.

Now they were going back through the long hall to the large room from which they had come. Laura was led over to a low chair near her father and the tall man and given a cup of milk and a cookie. When she had finished eating, she sat quietly in her chair.

Then she felt people getting up around her. Her father leaned down and patted her. Laura started to jump up. That pat usually meant that he was going away. His firm hand pushed her back down into the chair again. Now her mother leaned over and patted her.

Laura was terrified. This, too, was a good-by pat. Surely her father and mother were not going away! Surely they were not going to leave her in a strange place! Laura struggled to get out of the chair. But now it was the large hand of the friendly man and the gentle hand of the woman that were holding her back.

Laura felt a door close. She was allowed to get out of the chair, and she rushed madly in the direction in which she knew the door lay. It was closed. Laura let out a loud, unpleasant sound. It sounded almost like a wounded animal. She began crying and pounding on the door with her little fists.

"We must let her tire herself out some with her grief and tears," said Dr. Howe to his sister. "She is already tired from the long journey, and the fear and sorrow of this separation will exhaust her further. In a little while we must take her to her room. Her box of treasures and her clothes at least will be familiar to her."

"Oh, Sam, it is so pathetic to see her frightened and upset," said Miss Jeannette. "If there were only some way to let her know that it is all for her own good that she has come here." Dr. Howe and his sister watched the terrified little girl crying, beating the door, feeling about the room for some familiar object or person. When she came near them, they tried to comfort her, but each time she would draw away.

At last, when they felt that Laura would allow it, they led her to her room. They left her there and locked the door. When Miss Jeannette returned in less than half an hour, she found Laura sound asleep on her bed.

"We can expect that there will be several more scenes like the one we have just witnessed before Laura will accept the fact that she must stay here," said Dr. Howe to his sister.

"Of course!" said Miss Jeannette. "Can you imagine how she must feel? Suddenly, with no warning—for how could anyone warn her?—she has been taken from the familiar surroundings of the farm, separated from her father, her mother, her little brothers, and her good friend Mr. Tenney. Why, it is as if she had been suddenly plunged into an even darker prison than the one she has always lived in—still no light, no sound, almost no smells or tastes, and now not even the familiar things and people around her to touch!"

"I had thought of having Mrs. Bridgman remain here at the school for a few days," said Dr. Howe. "But I decided that since Laura is so bright and friendly, she would recover from the shock of separation quickly, and I could begin her education sooner if we did not have to wean her gradually from her mother. I hope I am not wrong about this."

"She *is* bright and friendly, Sam," said Miss Jeannette enthusiastically. "I could see that even in the little while before her parents left."

And Dr. Howe was right in thinking that Laura would quickly recover from the first shock of separation. In less than a week Laura began to be her own lively self once more. She began to reach out with her wonderful hands to learn all she could about her new home.

The room that had been given to Laura was in Dr. Howe's own apartment, and he and his sister quickly became another father and mother to her.

There were more than forty people at the school —blind children and teachers. Laura soon knew every one of them by touch.

After two weeks she was so happy in her new surroundings that Dr. Howe felt he could begin the experiment he had planned. Before he began, he discussed his plans with his sister.

"My goal is perfectly clear to me, Jeannette," he said. "I am going to try to bring into Laura's mind the idea that there are twenty-six different signs or letters that everyone uses. This is our alphabet. I want her to know that by combining these letters into words, we can share our thoughts with each other."

"But, Sam, how in the world are you going to 'tell' Laura that?" asked Miss Jeannette, puzzled. "If she were just blind, you could have her feel the raised-up letters with her fingers and tell her their names. Or, if she were just deaf and mute, you could show her letters. But she is blind and deaf and mute, so what can you do?"

"I know just exactly how I am going to try to do it," said Dr. Howe, smiling. "You may attend the first class with Laura tomorrow morning and see for yourself."

The great day dawned. When the first lesson began, Laura was seated at a table across from Dr. Howe. Beside her sat Miss Drew, who was to be Laura's own special teacher. Miss Jeannette Howe sat watching nearby.

The doctor had arranged a row of objects on the table in front of him. There were a large key, a spoon, a knife, a fork, a book, a cup, and a few other things that he felt sure Laura would know.

First Dr. Howe put the key into Laura's hand. It was a very large key. He let her handle it and feel it all over. She knew immediately what it was. The key at home with which she locked her boot in the cupboard was very much like this one— except for one thing. Her sensitive fingers paused as they felt the long key. There was something *on* this one.

Dr. Howe had fastened a paper label on the key. On the label the word *key* was written in a special kind of raised lettering or embossing that was used at that time in writing for the blind. The Braille system, which is now so widely used, had not yet been adopted. Dr. Howe guided Laura's fingers over the raised lines of the letters several times. Laura had no idea, of course, what these letters were.

Then he took the key away from Laura and handed her a spoon. She took it, felt it, and immediately recognized it as a spoon much like the ones with which she set the table at home. Again there was one important difference. Along the handle of the spoon Dr. Howe had pasted a label with the letters S-P-O-O-N written in raised type. Dr. Howe guided her fingers carefully over this word several times.

Now the doctor took away the spoon and gave her back the key. He directed her fingers to the label on the key again. Then he gave the spoon back to Laura and directed her fingers to the label on the spoon once more. He wanted her to feel that the shape of the lines on the key label and the shape of the lines on the spoon label were just as different from each other as the key and spoon themselves were different from one another.

Somewhere, thought Laura, I have felt lines like these. Was it on the plate Uncle Asa gave me?

Now the doctor did something else. He took away the key and the spoon and gave Laura just a piece of paper with some raised letters on it. The letters were K-E-Y again. Taking the key once more, Dr. Howe directed Laura's fingers to the label on it.

An expression on Laura's face made it quite clear that she recognized that the raised letters were the same on both papers, the one on the key and the separate label. Dr. Howe went through the same process with the spoon and a separate label that read S-P-O-O-N.

The rest of that first lesson was spent letting Laura feel the remaining objects—cup, knife, book, and so forth—and the labels for these, both those pasted on the object and those that were separate. From that time on Laura had lessons every morning and afternoon. She seemed to enjoy them thoroughly and to consider them just a game, not work. It was difficult for Dr. Howe and Miss Drew to get her to stop "playing" this game.

By about the third day Dr. Howe and Miss Drew were delighted to see that Laura had grasped the important point that the separate label for *key* somehow went with the key and the label that was separate from the spoon went with the spoon. That she understood this was shown by the fact that she could take a separate label, such as the one spelling *book*, and feel about until she found a book without any label. Then she would place the label on the book.

In a very few days Laura could reverse this process. She could pick up an object such as a spoon, search through a pile of loose labels on the table, feel them until she found the one that read S-P-O-O-N, and then place it on the spoon. She could do this for any object for which she had been taught the feeling of the word.

Dr. Howe was greatly encouraged. He felt sure that he was going to succeed with Laura; his only question was how long it was going to take him. In a report that he once wrote about his work with her he said: "It sometimes occurred to me that she was like a person alone and helpless in a deep, dark, still pit, and that I was letting down a cord and dangling it about, in hopes she might find it, and that finally she would seize it by chance, and, clinging to it, be drawn up by it into the light of day and into human society."

The lessons were going so well that Dr. Howe felt Laura was ready to take another important step forward. He had Miss Drew cut the labels for the words *key*, *spoon*, *knife*, and so forth, into separate letters. Up until this time Laura had seen words as wholes. Now he wanted her to learn that they are made up of parts—letters. Laura was allowed to follow closely, with her hands, all that Miss Drew did. After the words had been cut into separate letters, her hands followed Miss Drew's as she arranged the letters back into words.

In an astonishingly short time Laura had grasped the point of this new "game." If Miss Drew handed her the letters O, S, N, O, P, in a flash Laura could arrange them in the correct order to spell *spoon*. If Miss Drew gave her Y, K, E, Laura arranged them into the word *key*. O, K, O, B and I, K, E, N, F were equally simple for her. After a few more lessons Laura could do this with all the words in her vocabulary, and soon after that she could take from a pile of loose letters whatever ones she wanted and spell correctly

any word she wished of those that she had been
taught. This would have been a great accomplish-
ment for any eight-year-old. How much more
remarkable it was for a little girl like Laura
Bridgman!

Dr. Howe thought it would be easier for Laura
to arrange the letters if there were some kind of
form into which they could be fitted. Therefore he
had metal letters—types, he called them—made
for her and a frame with grooves into which the
letters could be fitted. He had four complete sets
made of the twenty-six letters of the alphabet.

Within a short time Laura was using the metal letters to build all the words she knew.

Two months had passed before Dr. Howe felt that Laura was ready to take the final step that he had planned for her. Miss Drew was sent to the home of a Mr. George Loring, who was a deaf-mute, to learn the manual alphabet. She learned it in one afternoon.

The manual alphabet is a way of forming the twenty-six letters of the alphabet with the hands. In the United States the one-handed manual alphabet is used. There is also a two-handed system used in some countries. In the one-handed system the letter *a*, for example, is formed by folding the four fingers over and keeping the thumb straight. *B* is formed by holding the fingers straight up with the thumb folded in. In only a few cases, as with *c* and *y*, for example, does the hand form a shape that very much resembles the shape of that letter as we write it.

A deaf person who has been "talking" with the manual alphabet for a long time can "say" as many as 130 words a minute. A deaf person who is skilled at watching another person "speak" with his hands can easily "read" 130 words a minute.

Laura, of course, would not be able to see the letters. Miss Drew would have to form them in Laura's hand so that she could feel them.

But how could she teach Laura that the various positions in which she held her fingers meant the letters of the alphabet that she had already learned with raised letters and metal types? This is how Miss Drew did it. She picked up the key and let Laura feel it. Then she took the letter K from the set of metal types and let Laura feel that. Then she shaped the letter *k* in the manual alphabet into Laura's hand, her first two fingers up and bent forward, the next two fingers folded down and the thumb up. She made Laura feel the way her fingers were held. Then she let Laura feel the metal letter K again.

The same procedure was followed with the letter *e*. First Laura must feel the metal type of the E, then Miss Drew formed *e* in the manual alphabet, all the fingers folded over and the thumb folded down, and then back to the metal type again. Finally the letter Y was taken from the metal types and Laura allowed to feel it. The manual *y* is formed with thumb up, little finger up, and other fingers all folded down. This one almost looks like a *y* as we write it. Now Miss Drew had set the metal types K-E-Y in the form. She let Laura run her hand over the whole word. Then she formed again, in the manual alphabet, the letters *k-e-y* in Laura's hand, and she placed the key itself in Laura's other hand. This was done with the spoon, the cup, and the key again.

And then it happened! For two months Laura had been "playing" these games with letters and words almost the way a trained dog performs

certain tricks. Now, suddenly, it was different. Dr. Howe always said that he knew almost the exact moment when Laura's face showed that she at last really understood what all this meant. Suddenly it seemed to become clear to her that every object had a name, that these names could be spelled by letters, either in raised letters, metal types, or, most easily of all, by the manual alphabet.

In one of his yearly reports about his work with Laura Bridgman, Dr. Howe wrote:

> . . . Now the truth began to flash upon her, her intellect began to work, she perceived that here was a way by which she could herself make up a sign of anything that was in her own mind, and show it to another mind, and at once her countenance lighted up with a human expression . . . I could almost fix upon the moment when this truth dawned upon her mind and spread its light to her countenance. . . .

Laura had found the rope that Dr. Howe was dangling before her. She had caught hold of it at last and could be drawn up from the dark pit in which she lived into the light of day!

What a different world it was for Laura now!

Can you imagine what it must have been like for her? She had been alive for eight years, and yet until this day she had never been able really to ask a single question! Now, suddenly, she could ask at least one enormous question: WHAT IS THE NAME OF THAT?

Of course she didn't know the words *what*, *is*, *the*, *name*, *of*, and *that*, but now by placing her hand on any object, she let her teacher know that she was asking for the name of that object.

And ask she did! At supper on the day she really understood that every object has a name, poor Miss Drew didn't get a bite to eat. Laura wanted the name of everything and everybody.

Usually at meals Miss Drew was expected to help not only Laura but several of the little blind girls. She cut their meat, buttered their bread, and did anything else that needed doing. But tonight Laura demanded every single bit of Miss Drew's attention.

"I'll help with the other children," said Miss Jeannette. "This one meal we'll let Laura have you wholly to herself. It's a kind of birthday for her."

And so Laura began. She placed her hand on her napkin, and Miss Drew spelled "napkin" into Laura's hand. Then Laura spelled it into Miss

Drew's hand. Then she asked the name of the tablecloth, the salt, the pepper, the sugar, the milk, and on and on and on. Miss Drew was thoroughly exhausted when she went to bed that night, and the muscles of her spelling hand ached for hours.

Soon after her arrival at the school Laura had been given a real doll to play with. Now she taught the doll the manual alphabet. Of course Laura had to pretend that the doll had fingers that could move. She also taught the manual

alphabet to many of the blind children so that they could talk with her.

When Laura had learned over one hundred common names of things, her teacher decided that it was time for her to learn another kind of word. Words that tell the names of things are called nouns. Miss Drew felt that Laura was ready to learn action words, or verbs as they are called.

For her first lesson in verbs Miss Drew led Laura over to the door. She let Laura feel her shut it. Then she spelled "shut door" into Laura's hand. Laura already knew the word *door*. She wondered at first what a "shut" was. Then Miss Drew opened the door. Then she spelled "open door" into Laura's hand.

It did not take Laura very long to understand that the words *shut* and *open* described what Miss Drew was doing to the door. Before the lesson was over, Laura showed that she had understood perfectly. She went over to a window and opened it. Then she spelled "open window" in the manual alphabet. Then she shut the window and spelled "shut window." In this way Laura very quickly learned the most common verbs, like *open, shut, come, go, run, walk, sleep, eat,* and so on.

The next kind of words that Miss Drew taught Laura was what are called adjectives, words that tell us something about an object. Words like *soft, hard, smooth, rough, sharp* are all adjectives. Very soon Laura knew that among the treasures she had brought from home were a *smooth* stone, a *sharp* porcupine quill, *soft* milkweed silk, and a *spiral* snail shell.

There are many other kinds of words besides nouns, verbs, and adjectives that Laura needed to know in order to talk in sentences. There are words like *in, on,* and *under* that are called prepositions; words like *soon, very,* and *there,* which are adverbs; connecting words like *and, or,* and *but;* and the little words *a, an,* and *the,* which are called articles.

Some of these words were very difficult for Laura to learn because they were not names of things, or things she could feel, or things her teacher could do. The only way for Laura to learn many of these words was to have other people use them and to use them herself.

Laura began making sentences simply by putting her words together in the order of what was most important to her. "Bread give Laura" was what she said when she wanted someone to give her a piece of bread. "Water drink Laura" of course meant that she wanted a drink of water, not that the water was going to drink her!

Every little child talks in this way at first. But as he listens to other people, he gradually learns to put his words together in the way they do. But Laura could not hear people talking around her. If Miss Drew had had the time to "talk" into Laura's hand for many hours a day, Laura would have learned what we call grammar and sentence construction much more quickly. But Miss Drew did not have time to do this, nor did she realize how important it was.

Laura did as well as she could, but her sentences never sounded just right. For example, in 1840 after one of her visits back to Hanover to see her family, she wrote: "When Laura did go to see mother, ride did make Laura side ache; horse was wrong, did not run softly."

It was not just the way we make our sentences that was a problem to Laura; the words themselves presented her with many difficulties also. One day Miss Drew was teaching Laura the words *right* and *left*. To teach this, she touched her own right hand and spelled "right hand" in the manual

alphabet. She repeated this for her left hand, for both her feet, her ears, and her eyes.

Bright little Laura understood it all. But then she had a question. She touched her own nose. She looked at her teacher with a puzzled expression. What was her nose? Right? Or left? What could Miss Drew say? What would you have said?

Laura very soon experimented with making up words. One day when she did not feel like doing her lessons, she told Miss Drew, "I feel very strongless." Miss Drew told her that there was no such word.

"But," said Laura, "when I do not sit still, you tell me that I am restless. Why can I not say I am strongless when I do not feel strong?"

"That just isn't a word," explained Miss Drew patiently.

"All right, then," said Laura, "I am very weakful!"

Poor Miss Drew had to explain that that was not a word either.

On another day Laura had been asked to take a message to someone and to go *alone*. The teacher explained that *alone* meant "by herself." Laura did as she was told and returned.

A little while later she thought of somewhere else she wished to go. This time she wanted to take one of her blind friends with her.

"Laura will go altwo," she said brightly. She had figured out that if al*one* meant by herself, al*two* meant with someone else.

She was very confused when a word that she already knew occurred as part of a longer word. One day after the school had moved to South Boston, which is near the ocean, she and Miss Drew were standing on the beach. The waves were crashing, and Laura asked what made the sand shake under her feet. "The waves are jarring the ground," said Miss Drew.

"Who put jar in the ground?" asked Laura.

In spite of such difficulties, Laura made wonderful progress, and before long she was reading the books in raised type that were used by the blind students in the school. Reading presented her with new problems. For one thing, she would read along in a sentence and try to understand it word by word instead of reading the whole sentence to find the meaning.

In a book written by Dr. Howe for the blind children, part of one sentence bothered her every time she read it. The sentence was: "You must not think because you are blind that you can not learn as much as other children."

When Laura read it, she would read: "You must not think because you are blind——" Here she would stop. With a worried look on her little face, spelling into Miss Drew's hand, she would ask, "Why did the doctor tell blind girls they must not think?"

Laura was soon ready to start arithmetic, and she did very well. But when she was old enough to do problems, she could not understand that the problems were not written especially for her and that she was just supposed to do the arithmetic in them.

Once a problem was read to her: "If you can buy a barrel of cider for four dollars, how much can you buy for one dollar?"

After thinking a minute, she asked, "How did the man who wrote the book know I was here?" And then she added, "I cannot give much for cider because it is very sour."

When Laura first started to study geography, it was naturally very difficult for her to imagine the tremendous size of our world or even the size

of our country. The blind children were taught their geography on relief maps on which the mountains were raised above the level of the rivers and valleys so that they could feel them. An enormous globe over thirteen feet in diameter was also used.

Still Laura had a very difficult time grasping the distances involved. One day her teacher was giving her a lesson about Niagara Falls. She was describing the great height of the falls and the loud noise the water made as it crashed down on the rocks below.

"Can you hear them now?" Laura asked.

"Oh, no!" said Miss Drew. "They are much too far away."

"Be very quiet," said Laura. "Listen carefully. Now don't you hear them?"

As Laura learned to "talk" and to "hear" with her hands, she discovered more and more about herself as well as about everything else. Gradually she learned how different she was from other people. She was told that other people talked with their mouths, saw with their eyes, and heard with their ears.

Strangely enough, she did not seem upset that she could not do all of these things. When she asked Miss Drew one day what *voice* meant, her teacher explained that voice is the noise people make when they talk with their mouths.

Laura thought for a minute. "I do not voice," she said.

One thing about her many handicaps did bother her, however. She did not like it one bit when she learned that dogs, which she considered inferior to people, could hear when people spoke with their mouths, but that she, a person, could not. That did not seem right to her.

As the years passed, Laura Bridgman studied every subject that other children study, and in all of her subjects she showed a keen mind and eager curiosity. Dr. Howe, Professor Mussey, James Barrett, Asa Tenney, and her own mother and father had all been right about Laura. She was a very bright little girl.

Many of Laura's teachers kept careful records during the years they spent working with her. Here are a few of the questions that Laura asked them. How many could you have answered if you had been the teacher?

"Who made water?"

"Why do not our hearts stop?"

"Why has fish not legs?"

"Why do not flies and horses go to bed?"

"Why does it rain?"

"Do *think, guess, suppose, understand* all mean the same?"

"Are there people in the sun?"

"Can flies go up to the sun?"

"How do we know there is air?"

"What is wind made of?"

"Why does a waterfall not stop?"

"Is God ever surprised?"

It was not long before the name of Laura Bridgman had become known all over the United States and parts of Europe. There were two reasons for this.

Dr. Howe, as director of the school, wrote each year a report of the progress of his work. He was so enthusiastic that what he wrote made exciting reading. It was even more exciting after he began his work with Laura Bridgman. Before many years had passed, Dr. Howe's annual reports were as eagerly awaited as a fascinating new book.

Dr. Howe also began the practice of holding an open house at the school on the first Saturday of each month. He did this because he was eager to have people see for themselves how much his blind students could learn. When he had begun his work, most people did not really believe that blind children could be educated.

And so on the first Saturday of each month the doors of the school were thrown open to anyone interested enough to walk in. Before long, hundreds of people were coming to these monthly "exhibits," as they were called. Here the public could see and hear blind children reading books printed in raised type. They could watch blind children work their arithmetic problems on special metal cases that had been developed for this purpose.

They could watch and listen as the children recited their geography lessons, tracing with their sensitive hands the mountains and rivers on the relief maps and huge globes that Dr. Howe had had made for them. Other students spun, wove, played on a variety of musical instruments, and did almost anything that seeing children could do.

Dr. Howe felt sure that if the public, whose tax money helped pay for this work, saw how much the blind could do, they would be more willing to give money for these purposes. He also arranged at different times to take some of the pupils before the state legislature, the men who decide how taxes

should be spent, so that they, too, could know and care about the work being done with the blind.

By 1839 Laura Bridgman had become one of the main attractions at the exhibits. Thanks to Dr. Howe's reports and the newspaper stories that were written about these reports, thousands of people began coming to the monthly exhibits to see this remarkable little girl.

Indeed, before long, such crowds gathered around Laura as she sat demonstrating her sewing, or her skill in arithmetic, or her ability to write with a regular paper and pencil, that her teachers thought it best to surround her desk with benches. In this way a little enclosure was made that held back the crowd and kept them from pressing in too closely.

The first time this was done Laura did not like it. She thought it was done to keep her from harming the people, not the people from harming her. She asked, "Are the ladies afraid of me?"

In 1842, when Laura was thirteen years old, one of the most famous men in the world at that time came on a visit from England to America. His name was Charles Dickens. He was an author whose books are still read and loved. Some of his best-known works are *David Copperfield, Oliver Twist,* and *A Christmas Carol.*

There was one person in the United States whom he wanted to be sure to see, and that was Laura Bridgman. He had read Dr. Howe's reports about Laura, and he wanted to see this unusual child himself.

After his visit with her at the school he wrote about her in his book *American Notes*. Charles Dickens was one of the most widely read authors of his day, so the name of Laura Bridgman became even more famous as a result of his story about her.

But there was another even more wonderful result. About forty years after Dickens made his visit, the mother of another little deaf, blind, and mute girl in Alabama read his account. This woman's daughter, Helen Keller, was about six years old at the time.

Like Laura Bridgman, Helen had become deaf and blind from a raging fever at about the age of two. Like Laura, because of an unusually bright and active mind, Helen was becoming by the age of six much too difficult for her parents to control.

When Mrs. Keller read the story of Dr. Howe's successful educational experiment with Laura Bridgman in Dickens's *American Notes*, she suggested to her husband that they write to Perkins Institution for help. Dr. Alexander Graham Bell, the inventor of the telephone, who had been a teacher of the deaf for many years and who had seen little Helen Keller, also suggested that they turn to Perkins for help.

And so a teacher was chosen—Anne Mansfield Sullivan. In preparing herself for this difficult job, Miss Sullivan spent long hours reading the records that Dr. Howe, Miss Drew, and other teachers had kept of their work with Laura Bridgman. When Miss Sullivan left for Alabama, she took in her suitcase a doll that Laura Bridgman, who was still living at Perkins Institution, had dressed especially for Helen. Two years later Miss Sullivan and Helen went to Boston to visit Perkins, and Helen actually met Laura Bridgman.

Ten years after Laura went to Perkins, her dear friend Asa Tenney died. She had returned home for visits every year and had always spent some time with Uncle Asa. For some reason, he never let her teach him the manual alphabet. Laura never forgot how much she owed to this dear friend of her childhood. A few years after his death she was asked to write a story about her life before she was educated by Dr. Howe. In the story Laura had a good deal to say about Asa Tenney. Here is what she wrote.

I had a small thin plate for my own, it was a gift from an old man named Mr. Asa Tenney whom I always loved. . . . The nice tin plate had the finger alphabet printed in raised letters around on the edge. . . . Mr. Tenney was always very patient and kind and gentle to me. [He] always dressed in most simple and frugal clothes . . . I derived a great pleasure from walking and rambling and sporting with Mr. T. daily. He used to go with me out of the doors in search of eggs very frequently. I liked so much to grope in hollowed nests with my little hands, seeking for a single egg.

. . . He influenced me with something like geography, which was, that I flinged sand, stones and gravels and branches of aged trees into the brook. I enjoyed that game extremely . . . He was stout and firm to lift me up in his big arms a long distance from place to place. I admired very much to be carried in his arms like a babe. We went out to pluck lots of different berries . . . Mr. T. never liked to scold me for doing a little thing which was really wrong according to his opinion. He never inflicted a punishment upon me in his life.

Laura Bridgman's other great friend, Dr. Samuel Gridley Howe, died in 1876. She realized how much she owed this great man also. After his death she wrote to a friend, "I think of Dr. Howe day and night, with sorrow and gratitude and love and sincerity."

For fifty-two years Laura Bridgman lived at Perkins. Dr. Howe had arranged for her to have a room there as long as she lived. Through her sewing she was able to earn some money, and she was a real help in educating other deaf, blind, and mute children who came to the school.

On the fiftieth anniversary of her coming to Perkins Institute a great celebration was held with Laura as the guest of honor. Dr. Howe's wife, Julia Ward Howe, was in charge of the party. Mrs. Howe had become very famous herself because of the song she had written during the Civil War, "The Battle Hymn of the Republic." There was an enormous "birthday cake," speeches were made by many famous men, and parts of Dr. Howe's well-known reports were read. Two years later, at the age of sixty, Laura Bridgman died.

Dr. Howe once described the education of Laura Bridgman as "a sort of triumphal march." When we hear the words "triumphal march," most of us see a picture in our minds of a victorious army that has conquered a powerful enemy. We can almost hear them as they march past to stirring music with bright banners waving.

It seems strange to think of the education of a little deaf, blind, and mute child as being anything like that. And yet, Laura Bridgman, with the help of Dr. Howe, Dr. Mussey, James Barrett, and Asa Tenney, had conquered the enemies of darkness and silence. They had done it in the same way that a lighted candle conquers the darkness of the silent night.

Think It Over

1. What do we call a story written about the life of a real person? Why do you think a book like this was written about Laura Bridgman?
2. What do you think the title *Child of the Silent Night* means?
3. What did Mr. Tenney mean when he said that Laura was living in a room without windows and doors? How did he make these for her?
4. Why did Laura's mother have so little time to give to her? What were some of Mrs. Bridgman's duties? Which ones were similar to Mrs. Shrawder's duties in *Skippack School?*
5. Where was Laura sent to school? Tell some of the ways Dr. Howe and Miss Drew taught her.
6. How did Dr. Howe get other people to know and care about the work of the blind?
7. What famous man came from England to America and asked to see Laura?
8. How did Laura's training help Helen Keller?
9. How long did Laura live at Perkins Institute? What did Laura do there that helped others?
10. Dr. Howe describes Laura's education as a "triumphal march." What did he mean?

Writing About Real People

Write a short biography of some person you know or love. Think of all the things others would like to know about the person that you choose. Be sure to remember in what way biographies are different from other stories.

Discovering New Words

Read the sentences that follow and write your own definition for each underlined word. The rest of the sentence sometimes gives you a clue to the meaning of the word. You may use your dictionary to check your answers.

1. If Mrs. Bridgman were making bread and <u>kneading</u> the dough, Laura would place her hands on her mother's arms and knead it with her.
2. "He [Mr. Tenney] has probably found many ways to <u>communicate</u> with her other than through words."
3. He held back the long blackberry <u>brambles</u> and guided Laura carefully.

4. "Jeannette, you know how eager I have been to find a child like this and to <u>experiment</u> with some of my ideas about the education of the deaf-blind."

5. "My <u>goal</u> is perfectly clear to me, Jeannette," he said. "I am going to try to bring into Laura's mind the idea that there are twenty-six different signs or letters that everyone uses."

What Is the Word?

What word or words complete the sentences? If you can't remember the words used in the book, turn back to the page given after each sentence.

1. A person who cannot talk is called _____.
   (page 331)
2. Laura's father was a _____.
   (page 333)
3. Laura's mother spun and wove _____.
   (page 333)
4. Uncle Asa often took Laura on _____.
   (page 336)

More Books to Read

D'AULAIRE, INGRI and EDGAR PARIN. *Buffalo Bill.*
Garden City: Doubleday & Company, Inc., 1952.

This is a beautifully illustrated biography of Bill Cody, famous American frontier scout and showman. No one led a more exciting life than he did in the days of wagon trains, buffalo herds, and the first railroads.

BULLA, CLYDE ROBERT. *Squanto, Friend of the White Men.*
New York: Thomas Y. Crowell Company, 1954.

Most of you have either heard or read about Squanto, the friendly Indian who helped the Pilgrims through their first hard winter. In this biography you will learn why he was able to speak English, and why he had no fear of the white men.

HOLBERG, RUTH LANGLAND. *Abigail Adams.*
Evanston: Harper & Row, Pubs., Inc., 1950.

Abigail Adams was the only woman to be the wife of one president and the mother of another. This interesting biography of Abigail Adams tells us much about life in the early days of our country.

Julia Cunningham was born in Spokane, Washington, but grew up in New York City. She loved books and make-believe, and always wanted to be a writer. Today she works in a bookstore in Santa Barbara, California, and writes every free moment she has.

Miss Cunningham says that she has arrived at one simple conclusion: ". . . living, as well as writing, is not only hard work but a joy, and both together create gladness and, sometimes, a good book." She believes that a good book comes when the author shares love and respect with her characters. Then, Miss Cunningham says, the characters will write the book for you.

MACAROON

JULIA CUNNINGHAM
ILLUSTRATED BY EVALINE NESS

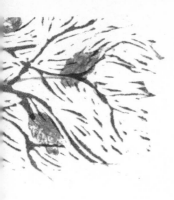

MACAROON

by Julia Cunningham

Illustrated by Evaline Ness

PANTHEON

Take a raccoon who doesn't want
to be loved. Then add an impossible,
disagreeable child, and you have
the makings of a wonderfully unhappy relationship. That, in fact,
was what the raccoon thought he
wanted. So it was with this idea
in mind that he trudged up to the
big house on the high hill. He had
heard that a disagreeable little girl
lived there.

The raccoon seemed to have found
a perfect solution to his problem.
But what finally happened was as
much of a surprise to him as it
will be to you.

The very moment the raccoon opened his eyes he knew it was the day to decide. The pines of his forest gloomed dark against the almost brilliant oaks and maples hung with leaves of rose and pale yellow and green turning scarlet. His nose lifted to taste the air and found it already cinnamoned with autumn, already pungent with damp earth smells like the undersides of mushrooms. Even the tips of his delicate raccoon paws were no longer quite warm.

He had a problem. If this year were like every other year in his life, it would be easy enough to wander toward the village and simply wait for the first smiling child to catch him. A long winter sleep in a tree was not for him. As before, he would allow himself to be hugged and stroked and loved and taken into the child's home for the snow season, where the best place by the hearth would soon be his and his meals delivered to him in a special saucer. It was no trick at all to adopt a child. They liked him.

But all summer long the raccoon had thought of the many children he had abandoned on the first morning of spring, had heard their voices crying after him through the freedom of his freshened, newly greened woods; and he had, once or twice, been forced to hold his jaws tight between his fingers so that he wouldn't answer them and become imprisoned in their world forever. He had been haunted by each round, wide-eyed face, and he hadn't enjoyed the feeling. So this autumn all was to be different.

"I'm very positively not going to spend my nights holed up in a tree," he said to a very disinterested field mouse. "Nor am I going to give

up the soft rugs and the music in the evenings
and the lovely, sneezy smell of burning logs." He
glared at the mouse. "Do you hear me?" he said
sternly. "I'm just not!"

The mouse shyly bowed himself out of sight behind a log, and the raccoon was left alone with his troubles. A crow passed overhead and squawked something rude at the puzzled animal. The raccoon did not reply, but the ugly sound had given him an idea. Why not adopt a child so disagreeable, so impossible, that he would be happy to leave when the time came? He waved his forelegs in the frosty air, very pleased with himself, and then began to lope slowly toward the edge of the forest. How very clever he was! Ask a raccoon, and the answer was present before blinking. He paused to whack the dust out of his tail between two rocks, and then, surveying the countryside, now filled with barns and houses and standing horses, he looked out of his bright brown eyes for an impossible child.

At first there was only the empty peace of no people at all. Then he glimpsed an oncoming procession of small children going toward the schoolhouse in the distant village. He recognized some of them. He had lived in their rooms and slept in their beds. He felt a twinge of shame at the sight of them and supposed, quite rightly, that they were still wondering what had become of

their great friend the raccoon, and missing him dreadfully. None of these would do at all.

A lame fox crossed in front of him. He always spoke to foxes because they were almost as intelligent as he was.

"Good fox," he said, "have you ever met in these parts an impossible child?"

The fox halted just long enough to retort, "I'm hungry. All human creatures are impossible. You'd know that for yourself if you liked chicken dinners." And he limped swiftly away, throwing back out of the side of his bitter mouth, "Try the big house—they don't even keep chickens."

The raccoon ignored the discourtesy of the fox and, for lack of a better direction, began the three-mile journey to the mansion whose wide iron gates he could just see atop the highest hill in the valley. As he traveled, he remembered a few odd fragments of gossip he had heard. There was no cat or dog within the stone walls that bordered the mansion. He smiled. Maybe because the child was difficult—and now he did truly remember; a little girl lived there, though he had never seen her in anyone else's house. Once he had found a pair of skates tumbled at the bottom of the hill, as though they had been thrown away in anger. Well, it was worth investigating, and his hopes gave speed to his legs.

He had no sooner come within peering view of the tall drawing-room windows of the four-storied, turreted house than he realized that this was his lucky hour. A sound of scolding knifed across the vast porch from inside.

"I tell you, Erika, you'll be the death of me yet! You refuse the cook's very best luncheon, and now you tell me you're not going to take a nap. I can't punish you as you deserve because I am neither your father nor your mother."

444

The raccoon hopped onto the porch and pressed his right ear against the nearest pane of glass. Now he could hear the other voice, a smaller and higher one. It must be the child.

"A good thing you're not!" and the tones were even cranky enough to suit the raccoon's purposes. "I couldn't stand having them around me all the time."

He peeked in.

There stood a very thin, tired-eyed woman in a gray silk dress with a white collar, and just in front of her, her face as purple as a plum, a spindling little girl.

"I wonder," said the thin woman, who the listening animal guessed must be the governess, and her voice had lost its hard edges. "Well, you do as you like about the nap. But I am going to take one, and I shall expect you to preserve a decent silence."

He saw the governess leave the room, and the child begin to hop up and down, thumpingly, to the tune of "I Went to the Animal Fair."

The raccoon tapped on the window once, then twice, and at last the brittle noise penetrated the bump-blast of the song and dance.

The front door clicked open, and the child stepped out. At her first sight of the raccoon her face became plain white and pink again, and her eyes were momentarily startled.

"Who are you?" she asked, and then remembered to be disagreeable. "And what are you doing on my porch?"

He merely snarled at her.

For answer the little girl grunted to express her extreme disgust.

He clinked his teeth rapidly together.

The child's mouth changed into a false smile. "Won't you come in?" she said, moving to one side to allow him to pass. The raccoon knew she wanted to pull his ringed tail, and he was well content. This was a fine beginning to a difficult friendship, just the kind he wanted for the winter, one he would never regret breaking off in the springtime.

He was certain to come within easy reach of her hand, and as she grabbed for his tail, he nipped at and captured the end of her thumb. He held on, being careful not to hurt her.

"You rotten raccoon!" she squealed. "Let me go!"

He obeyed, but not before he saw the purple seep back into her cheeks. Then he stalked into the house and looked about him. The depth of the rugs was quite satisfactory, and the fireplace was large enough for twenty raccoons to take their repose in front of. The chairs were leather, the tables polished and smelling of cleanness, and

the lamps so many that his peculiar preference for spotlights would be well indulged.

"You act as though you planned to live here!" shouted the child indignantly.

"I do," stated the animal, speaking for the first time. "With your permission, of course," and he grinned so wickedly that he saw the shadow of a smile quirk up the corners of the child's lips. Two dimples almost formed at each side.

"You talk, too," said the child.

"I do to you," he replied, seating himself by the hearth so that she would recognize it as his place. "To no one else, so there's no use telling other people you have a talking raccoon in the house. It just causes curiosity and bother."

"It's a secret, you mean?"

He caught the glint of malice in her eyes. "No, not a secret. If it were, you would enjoy telling it simply to spite me. I know." He closed his eyes comfortably.

"Don't you dare go to sleep. That's what Miss Minks is doing, and I get bored when everyone's asleep but me."

When he did not respond, she tried again.

"Don't you want to know what my name is?"

"Later," said the raccoon, the taste of his power over this weasel of a child as sweet as a sugar lump.

"Not later—now!" and she stamped both feet. "It's Erika."

"That's a good prickly name. It suits you."

"It's not prickly at all! It's my mother's, and she's as soft as—as your fur!"

"In that case I apologize. Where is she? Anyone like my fur I would be pleased to meet."

The child hesitated. "I don't exactly know. Traveling. She takes pictures of famous people, and my father writes about them. They haven't much time to stay at home."

The raccoon opened his eyes. He didn't wish to let pity spoil his pleasantly unhappy relationship with this girl. If he did, it would all end as the others had, with regret and sorrow at parting.

"Let's not talk about them," he suggested. "How about a game?"

"What kind?" said Erika, thoroughly ready for mischief again.

"A banister race. Whoever gets down in the least time must give the other one a cookie. Macaroons, if you have any. They're my favorite kind."

"I hate macaroons—they leave a bad taste in my mouth, and so do you." She squeezed her eyes into slits. "But come on, you old macaroon. I'll play your silly game."

The raccoon shrugged. He didn't mind being called Macaroon. It sounded tasty enough to him.

For the next hour they slid swoopingly down the two-story banister, Erika carrying the raccoon on the upward journeys because he insisted on it. Neither could decide who won, so it ended in their both going into the kitchen.

The cook, a sour woman stuffed into a checked dress much too small for her, was not delighted to admit a raccoon into her kitchen. But she was afraid of Erika, and with very bad manners indeed slammed down a jar of cookies on the table.

The raccoon bowed his thanks to her, and the cook's face relaxed.

Erika grabbed two handfuls of cookies and went into the hall. Macaroon followed, his paws almost as crammed.

"I always wash before eating," he announced.

Erika made a spitting noise with her tongue and pointed to the high staircase that led to the bathroom. Macaroon reminded himself that he was not here to teach her manners—quite the opposite—and humped himself up the stairs.

He didn't need to search long because the scent of soap floated under the crack of a nearby door. He reached up the full length of his body, turned the knob, and walked in.

"Very pretty," he said to himself, admiring the rose-sprinkled wallpaper, the shining whiteness of the bathtub, and the ivory bristles of a tiny brush dangling by the washbasin. In five minutes he was drifting tranquilly up and down the tub now filled

with warm water, the cookies piled carefully beside
the toothbrush.

Two hours later, after a solid nap, Macaroon
emerged from what he now assumed was his room

and wandered downstairs. All was quiet in the wood-paneled entrance hall. The raccoon listened for some trace of Erika so that he could go where she wasn't. It was rather a nervous business trying not to be friends with someone, like always being on guard against tigers in an open field.

Suddenly two sets of giant claws descended upon his shoulders. He yelled and leaped up so high in the air that his tail swept a lamp off a nearby table. Trembling, he took refuge under a couch and peeped cautiously out. There stood Erika, laughing so hard that the bear rug in her arms sagged to the floor.

"Fooled you that time!" she shouted. "You thought I was a savage beast, didn't you?"

Haughtily Macaroon ambled out from his hiding place and began to smooth his fur. "You're worse than a pestilence," he muttered.

"If you mean a pest, that's just what I am," responded Erika. "And now I'm having dinner served in the formal dining room. You may come, too."

It wasn't long before Macaroon realized the reason for this lapse into graciousness, because all through the meal she pelted him with small

459

objects like green peas and bread crusts and, at the very last, walnut shells. And when the cook came to collect the plates, of course Erika let her think it was all the raccoon's fault.

The cook was not pleased. "We'll see no more of that filthy animal by tomorrow," she threatened.

"Why not, I'd like to know?" snapped Erika. "He's no affair of yours. This is my house."

"Is that right, missy? We'll just see, that's all!" and she stalked back to her kitchen.

With one hop Erika was at the long bellpull that hung by the sideboard. She yanked it five times. Macaroon waited. Who would answer this arrogant summons?

The door swung wide, and in rushed the governess. "Can't I even have any peace at mealtime?" she demanded. "You said you preferred to eat alone, and it has been a blessing to me. And now——" She caught sight of the raccoon, who eyed her firmly. "What on earth is *that* doing in your father's chair?"

"An enemy of mine," retorted Erika. "I invited him to stay with me."

"We'll see about that," said the tight-lipped Miss Minks. "After tomorrow," she added portentously.

Erika rooted herself directly in front of Miss Minks, so close that her nose almost brushed the tall woman's belt buckle. "What is all this about tomorrow? First the cook and now you. I command you to tell me!"

"No need to command anybody," said the governess with a twisted rise in her voice that made Macaroon's back hairs prickle. "Your father and mother are returning in the morning, and they'll soon put a stop to your nonsense about harboring a woods creature in the house."

"That's not true!" said Erika, her hands clenching and unclenching behind her back. "They want me to have everything I need to keep me happy!"

"And that's perhaps why they leave you alone with cook and me for most of the year?" said Miss Minks.

The sneer behind Miss Minks' words tempted Macaroon to nip holes in her stockings, but he remained motionless. This wasn't his battle or his concern, and the darker things got for Erika, the better. She deserved it as payment for her utter selfishness and absolutely perfect rudeness.

"You wait!" Erika was yelling now. "You just wait! I'll have them fire you the very first thing!"

"I think not," answered the governess. "I'm the only one who has stayed with you more than three weeks in five years."

At this, Erika gave such a grating roar of rage that Macaroon slid under the table for protection; and a good move it was, for suddenly the room flashed with a hail of plates and glasses that crashed haphazardly against the nearest obstacles. Then he saw Miss Minks seize Erika by the arms and drag the flurry of kicking, writhing child out of the room and up the stairs.

Macaroon didn't wait for the arrival of the cook—he was getting out, back to his forest. What if his paws did curl in cramps as he slept in his tree hole all winter? What if he did get thinner and thinner until he became a mere shadow of a raccoon? No amount of comfort and warmth and lamb chops was worth this stormy, hating mockery of a home. Well, he would just help himself to that charming brush in the bathroom and be on his way.

As he passed Erika's door, he heard the shrieks dwindle to an out-of-breath kind of panting that hunted animals make when they have run too far for their strength.

This short pause was Macaroon's undoing. By the time the governess had gone down the stairs, never seeing the deep darkness of the raccoon flattened against the wall, the sound coming from behind Erika's closed door had changed. Macaroon tried very hard not to listen, but his ears were as keen as thorns, and the sound crept in. Erika was crying. And even then Macaroon would not have broken his trip back to the peace and chill of his forest if he hadn't recognized the difference between crying for anger and crying for sadness, and Erika's was all sadness.

Irritated with himself, he gently turned the knob of Erika's door and went in.

Erika took one look at Macaroon from her red-lidded, tear-splashed eyes and spluttered, "Get out! Get out of here!"

The raccoon gazed at her solemnly, then closed the door behind him and walked to the window. He pried it up just far enough so that he could squeeze through. The sobbing and the heaving had ceased. Now came a series of sniffs and gulps and throat-clearings.

He balanced himself on the window sill and was about to reach for the nearest branch of the tree just outside when a choky voice stopped him.

"Where are you going?" said the voice, as unlike Erika's as a lark's is unlike a gull's.

"Back home," said the raccoon, and instead of climbing into the tree, he scratched himself under the chin where it didn't itch, just to give her more time.

"I'm going with you," said the child, and without waiting for his consent, she hurriedly thrust on her heaviest sweater and tied a red scarf around her neck.

"Nobody wants me," she continued, "so I don't want anybody."

"And how do you know I want you?" asked Macaroon.

"Maybe you don't, but I'm coming with you anyway."

Something warned the raccoon that this was the instant to refuse, to tell her flatly that life in the winter forest was complicated enough without the burden of this most impossible of all impossible children. He still had a choice. He must abandon her or tame her. Then he remembered the sound that was all sadness, and he chose.

"I don't like the idea," he said, "but—well, come along." And without further delay he led the way to the stairs. "You'll be hungry before night," he whispered as they reached the front door. "You'd better go get some food from the kitchen without the cook's knowing it."

"Oh, I'll get the food all right," said Erika. "Cook is accustomed to doing what I tell her."

The raccoon shook his head, doubting all over again the wisdom of his choice, but he did not use her absence to run away and leave her. In three minutes Erika appeared, carrying a large picnic basket loaded with bread, cold chicken, and cheese, and the two of them escaped unseen from the house and trotted together into the forest.

"Where is your house?" Erika said finally, after they had walked what seemed to be at least two miles.

"House?" said the raccoon. "I live in a tree."

"Oh, a treehouse."

"No. A hole in a tree."

"Is it big enough for me, too?"

"Hardly."

"Then where will I sleep?"

Macaroon wished he didn't have to answer this, because he didn't know.

"We'll let that take care of itself when the time comes for sleeping," he replied, and wished that he had had sense enough to adopt nobody this autumn.

"I know. I'll find a cave—the kind bears live in." Erika's idea of how bears live had come out of a book, where their houses were completely furnished with tables and chairs and hot cereal. For a while this thought kept the mounting chill of night from penetrating too far into her sweater. But when they at last arrived at the raccoon's oak tree, all she wanted was a fireplace and a cup of cocoa.

"Let's have some supper," said Macaroon, seeing the child's nose crinkle in the first stage of a sneeze.

So Erika unlatched the basket, and they soon were chewing hungrily at hunks of bread with cheese between.

Erika shivered twice. "You have fur," she commented. "I haven't."

"I'd lend you some of mine, but I can't," said the raccoon, quite worried now and determined to urge her to return to her house. He had just opened his mouth to speak when out of the deepening shadows of tree trunk and underbrush limped the lame fox.

"Thought I smelled supper," said the fox, and he made a grab with his teeth at something in the basket.

Erika lunged at him and smashed the lid shut,

scraping the fox's nose hurtfully. "You can't have any!" she shouted, her own face more vixenish than the fox's.

The fox sat down on his haunches at a distance of five yards and looked sorrowfully at the raccoon, the girl, and the concealed chicken. "I'm very empty," he said. Then he looked directly at Erika. "You belong to people, don't you?"

"Am I a person, you mean? Yes, of course. Why?"

"I thought so. Just like all the others. You don't know how to share a chicken. Or anything else," he added, licking his lame foot.

Macaroon gave Erika a steely signal with both eyes. Erika was puzzled. She watched Macaroon divide his bread and cheese into two portions and hand one to the fox. Imperiously she waved back Macaroon's bread and cheese and dipped her hand into the basket and offered the fox a fat brown chicken leg.

But this time the fox did not grab. He hesitated. "No tricks?" he said, his nose quivering.

"No tricks," said Erika, and stretched out her hand and the chicken.

"Thank you," said the fox, and he quietly accepted the leg and began to crunch the sweet and buttery meat.

By the time the basket was vacant, it was true dark. Only Erika's white skin and the fox's tawny coat gleamed a little lighter than the blackened background of the woods.

"I sometimes smell snow nowadays," said the fox, to make conversation.

"Not tonight, surely," said the raccoon, sitting as close to Erika as he could because he knew the cold was entering her bones.

"No. But soon. I guess I'll be going along now."

But before he could say a final good night, the raccoon had an idea.

"Could you let Erika sleep in your den with you?" he said to the fox. "It would be warmer than just nowhere."

"Certainly," said the fox, content to return the favor of the chicken. "Follow me."

"I'm not going without Macaroon," said Erika firmly.

Macaroon stifled a giant sigh and trotted behind the procession of two. After all, he didn't really mind, for he loved to adventure through the night.

The fox's earth was just a few yards distant, and he plunged down and into the hole almost before Erika could spot it. She wriggled herself through a short tunnel and then popped out into a more spacious underground dugout.

"It smells!" she exclaimed, covering her nose with one hand.

"Naturally," said Macaroon, wishing for the hundredth time he had not accepted the job of reforming this impossible child. "Of musk and delicious fox scent." He poked her in the ribs with one elbow and was just about to pinch her ankle when she got the point.

"It's lovely," she added hastily, and breathed as shallowly as she could.

"Thank you," said the fox, and he curled himself into a round and closed his eyes.

Erika was silent for a few moments. Then she stretched full-length on the warm earth and whispered in Macaroon's nearest ear, "Do you think they've missed me at my house yet?"

"I'd guess they have," answered Macaroon. "Want to go back now?"

"Never!" hissed Erika. "The cook hates me, Miss Minks hates me, and so do the other two."

Macaroon knew she meant her father and mother. "I doubt that," he said as sturdily as a whisper would allow.

"I don't," Erika answered, still in a whisper. "If they didn't, why don't they ever come back except when they feel like it or are out of jobs? It's never because of me. Why, they didn't even turn up for Christmas. Is that what you call loving? Is it?"

Macaroon had very positive ideas on this subject, but he didn't want to share them with this child who was really no better off than an orphan. "They are coming tomorrow."

"For reasons of their own. Oh, maybe they'll be worried for a few days; but later, a week or so from now, they will look at each other and one of them might say, 'Remember when we used to have a child called Erika?' and the other will answer and say, 'Yes. Yes, I do. Wonder what ever befell her?'"

"Well, I'll tell you what is befalling me," said Macaroon. "Sleep."

He waved his tail in good night; then he turned his head in the direction of the entrance to the den where the air should have been fresher and wasn't, and soon he joined the fox in equal dreaming.

Erika had no other choice than to shut her eyes, but before she capsized into unconsciousness, she thought that just maybe she heard faraway shouts.

It was not yet dawn when the raccoon was jolted awake by the sharp strike of the fox's paw. "They're coming! They're coming!" half barked the fox.

Macaroon, quickened completely out of sleep, spoke back. "Who? Who's coming?"

"The dogs! They're coming to get me!"

"Be quiet!" ordered Macaroon, and he listened with such concentration that to his ears, too, arrived the distant, excited yelps of hounds. "But this isn't hunting country!" he exclaimed.

"Used to be in my grandfather's time," said the fox. "He told me. What can I do? I am lame. What on earth can I do?"

Macaroon flicked his tail across Erika's face, and she came alert almost as quickly as an animal. "What is it?" she said, aware that trouble had entered the den.

"The dogs are coming to get me!" said the fox, his breath already shortened.

"Nonsense," said the girl. "It's me they're after. Nobody hunts around here. In the first place nobody owns any riding horses." Then her face took on the same squeezed look as the fox's. "But they're not going to catch me."

She looked at the fox and the raccoon, and something in her eyes flowered for the first time; she was asking a favor of someone else, and she didn't know how.

Macaroon glanced at the fox, and the same answer was in his triangular face. "We will help you," he said. "Especially me. You shared your food with us. The fox shared his home. Now it's my turn." He raised his arms over his head as though addressing a parliament. "Now listen. The dogs have undoubtedly been given your scent, Erika, and in a few minutes they will arrive at the fox's earth." He pointed to the fox. "Just before they get here, you will go above ground and show yourself. No dog could ever resist chasing a fox. Then you will lead them off and away from here while Erika and I find another hiding place. We'll have to break her scent, so that means getting to the brook in the woods and wading downstream. You must give us enough time for that."

"I'll try," said the fox gallantly. "But how do I shake off the dogs?"

"When the people behind the dogs discover they are chasing a fox, they'll call them off."

"I most fervently hope so," said the fox.

"Stop hoping and start running," instructed the raccoon. "Those hounds are almost upon us."

With a salute of his bushy tail the fox vanished from the den. Macaroon and Erika could hear a tangled confusion of yips and barks and scrambling as the dogs changed course. When the upper regions were nearly silent, Macaroon nudged Erika. "We must go now," and they pushed themselves through the burrow and regained the outer world. A thick mist obscured all but the nearest trees. "We're in luck," whispered the raccoon. "Pick me up and I'll tell you where to go. It will be faster that way."

Erika grabbed the raccoon and began to race toward the center of the forest. Roots and ruts conspired to make her stumble, but she did not decrease her pace. "Keep going!" encouraged the raccoon, uncomfortably mashed against her collarbone

but resisting any complaint. "The stream is only a few yards more."

And when Erika finally reached the banks of the narrow waterway, she almost fell in. "Put me down," said Macaroon. "Now follow me." He half paddled, half walked through the rough rush of water, Erika splashing behind him.

Once the chorus of dogs whirled just a hundred feet away, but the fox still had them in hand.

"How much longer?" wheezed the child. "I'm freezing, and I've cut my shins all over."

"See that oak ahead?" spoke back the raccoon, still forging onward. "That's our refuge."

Erika couldn't see the oak because the fog was as dense as smoke, but she trusted the raccoon to know. At last she saw him clamber up the steep bank and disappear behind a thicket.

She stepped upward, slipped on the damp mud, and slid back into the stream. Drenched and shuddery, she drew herself upright again and, seizing the long grasses that beckoned at the top of the shallow ridge, hoisted and yanked and heaved until she found herself flat on her stomach on the wet ground. She sat up. "Macaroon, where are you?" she called.

Then she saw him, tall against the tree, and flopped down beside him.

Macaroon didn't wait for her to catch her breath. "I'm very worried," he said gravely.

"About me?"

"No, not about you. About the fox. He's got a game leg and is no longer young."

"What could happen to him? You said that as soon as they find out the dogs are chasing a fox, they will call them off."

"That's what I said, but I'm not at all sure it's happening that way." Macaroon's ears drooped, and his paws churned nervously together in the movements of washing. Then his paws stilled, and he looked at Erika with such intensity and for so long that her cheeks began to redden. She knew the raccoon was waiting for her to say something and also that that something must be just the right thing, not a comment on the weather or even a discussion of the problem. She tried to break away from his deep, deep look, but she couldn't. She tried not to think, but thoughts like the first approach of sky-borne birds winged into her mind, flying so close that she could almost hear the wind's flap on their feathers. Why had she run away?

Because no one loved her, and she was forced to be cross all the time. Why was she so cross? Why had she made life a torture for both the cook and Miss Minks? Why was she the way she was? How was she? The word loomed like a hawk and pounced—*impossible.*

Erika didn't know why, but suddenly she felt like crying, not for sadness but for another kind of feeling that made her body strong and new. "Come on!" she cried. "We have to find the fox!"

Just at that instant such a tempest of legs and tails and snarls and barks whirled around them that Erika was knocked flat on her back. The five dogs scrabbled over and around her, intent on bringing down a very ragged, tawny specter of a fox. She raised herself half up, shoved into the center of the furious tangle, and encircled the exhausted fox within her arms.

But what was the high, shrilling war cry that rang in her ears? Even the triumphant hounds checked their violence. It was Macaroon, standing straight up on his hind legs, daring the five great beasts to do battle. The first one who advanced never saw what tore a hunk of fur from his chest. The next received a gash the length of his foreleg.

Erika, still holding the fox, scrambled to one side and set him on all four feet. "Can you make it to your den?" she asked.

The fox's foam-splattered mouth formed one word, "Yes," and with that he staggered off into the mist.

Still the beleaguered raccoon held off the dogs, thrusting swift as the blade of a sword at his nearest attackers. But Erika knew that, surrounded as tightly as he was, it wouldn't be long before he fell under their jaws.

She ignored the cuts and bruises that splotched her hands and legs, and picking up a gnarled stick, she whacked at the dogs as hard as she could. But they were too intent on the slaughter of one of their oldest enemies, and the circle around the raccoon shrank like the closing of a noose.

"Nobody's going to hurt Macaroon!" she shouted, not caring for anything or anybody except the courageous little animal whose left ear was now scarlet with blood. "Nobody! Nobody!" She kicked her way through the dogs, seized him around the stomach, and held him high over her head. "Now kill me if you want to, but you'll never get Macaroon!"

Their prey removed from reaching distance, the dogs crouched and growled and paced but did not touch the girl. Erika, so shaky inside that her backbone seemed to be turning to clots of sand, walked right through the pack and started out of the forest.

Twice she felt the knick of teeth at her heels, and once she heard her dress rip at the edges; but she continued to walk slowly and steadily through the trees, Macaroon like a furry umbrella above her.

"Don't be afraid," she said to him as they passed through the last barrier of tree trunks and into the meadow that led to her house. "We are going home."

Macaroon carefully said nothing, and it wasn't entirely because she gripped him so tightly around the middle that he could scarcely breathe. He was so proud of his adopted child that there were no words at all to say, not ever.

They had no sooner gained the gates of the mansion than the dogs fell away and a small crowd of people poured toward them from around the corner of the house. One was Erika's mother. Another was her father. Even Miss Minks was there, sniffling into a very wet handkerchief. The others stood back with very trembly grins on their faces.

And just before they met, Erika halted and put Macaroon on the ground. "Are you all right?" she asked so no one else could hear. Macaroon nodded and put his left paw into her right hand. Together they faced this new problem of people.

Two people, a man and a woman, walked forward until they were within three feet of the child
and the raccoon. They hesitated, looked uncer-
tainly at one another, and then the woman put out
her hand toward Erika as though she weren't sure

she should touch her. Macaroon felt Erika's hand tighten around his paw. He raised his nose and brushed the back of her hand twice, trying to tell her to forgive. She understood, and extended her free arm to the woman.

Suddenly the child was enveloped in such a hugging and laughing and crying that Macaroon slid his paw from between her fingers. Now they were all three talking so fast, their words so jumbled and mixed and happy, that Macaroon had to laugh, too.

Then he knew it was time for him to leave. Erika had a family now, a family she was ready to love and live with. She wouldn't need him. He smiled a little wryly. Well, maybe his fur would thicken during the sleep-drugged nights of snow and frost. He shrugged, and then he knew his winter would be a good one. Just the thought of Erika, herself at last, would keep him warm and comforted.

He quietly turned about-face and said a silent farewell to his friend. He would miss her, more than all the rest lumped together, and he knew at that very instant that he would never again adopt anyone else. Erika was the last and the best.

But before his first step was taken, before he
even swallowed the first gulp of loneliness, someone kissed him right on top of his head and whispered in his torn ear, "Macaroon, we're both home.
And do you know what we'll do together first thing
tomorrow morning? Fill a basket with the most
wonderful feast in the world and invite the fox to
share it."

Macaroon did not speak. Instead, he smiled
straight into the wide happiness of her suddenly
lovely eyes.

Think It Over

1. The raccoon could always find a child to live with during the cold winter months, but still he had a problem. What was it?
2. What made the raccoon decide that the girl in the mansion was just the child he was looking for?
3. Why did he change the subject when Erika was talking about her parents?
4. How did Macaroon get his name?
5. On page 465 we learn that Macaroon could tell the difference between crying for anger and crying for sadness. Why do you think that Erika was crying "for sadness"?
6. What was her idea of a bear's house? From what book do you think she got this idea?
7. What made Erika decide to share her food with the fox?
8. When the dogs were heard outside the fox's den, what did Erika do that she had never done before? Why did the animals want to help her?
9. Do you think Erika was the same kind of child at the end of the book as at the beginning? If you think that she changed, tell how.

Which Words Would You Choose?

Put the words that tell the kind of person Erika was at the beginning and at the end of the book in two lists.

kind   pleasant   ugly
friendly   unhappy   rude
lonely   disagreeable   mischievous

Change the Word

Write the sentences below in your notebook, but change the underlined words to others that mean the same or almost the same.

1. He [Macaroon] began to lope slowly toward the edge of the forest.
2. In five minutes he was drifting tranquilly up and down the tub.
3. Macaroon ambled out from his hiding place.
4. Even the triumphant hounds checked their violence.
5. Irritated with himself, he gently turned the knob of Erika's door and went in.

More Books to Read

Cunningham, Julia. *Candle Tales.*
New York: Pantheon Books, 1964.
This is a book about six animals and an old man, and six nights of storytelling.

The Brothers Grimm. *The Traveling Musicians.**
New York: Harcourt, Brace & World, Inc., 1955.
Four animals traveling as musicians meet a gang of robbers with surprising results.

Haviland, Virginia. *Favorite Fairy Tales Told in France.**
Boston: Little, Brown and Company, 1959.
A collection of five famous fairy tales with especially beautiful illustrations.

Norton. Mary. *The Borrowers.*
New York: Harcourt, Brace & World, Inc., 1953.
A fanciful tale of some delightful little people called the Borrowers. You will not read far before you find out how they got their name.

Stolz, Mary. *Belling the Tiger.*
New York: Harper & Row, Pubs., Inc., 1961.
The smallest and least important mice are chosen to bell the house cat. Trouble begins for them, but fun begins for you.

*Included in *Invitations to Personal Reading*, Curriculum Foundation Classroom Library, Scott, Foresman and Company.